W9-AYH-623

HOMICIDAL PSYCHO JUNGLE CAT

Other Books by Bill Watterson

Calvin and Hobbes
Something Under the Bed Is Drooling
Yukon Ho!
Weirdos from Another Planet
Revenge of the Baby-Sat
Scientific Progress Goes "Boink"
Attack of the Deranged Mutant Killer Monster Snow Goons
The Days Are Just *Packed*
The Calvin and Hobbes Tenth Anniversary Book
There's Treasure Everywhere
It's a Magical World

Treasury Collections

The Essential Calvin and Hobbes
The Lazy Sunday Book
The Authoritative Calvin and Hobbes
The Indispensable Calvin and Hobbes

HOMICIDAL PSYCHO JUNGLE CAT

A Calvin and Hobbes Collection by Bill Watterson

Andrews McMeel
Publishing

Kansas City

 For information, write Andrews McMeel Publishing, an Andrews McMeel Universal company, 4520 Main Street, Kansas City, Missouri 64111.

ISBN: 0-7407-2299-9

Library of Congress Catalog Card Number: 94-71736

calvin and HOBBES

by WATTERSON

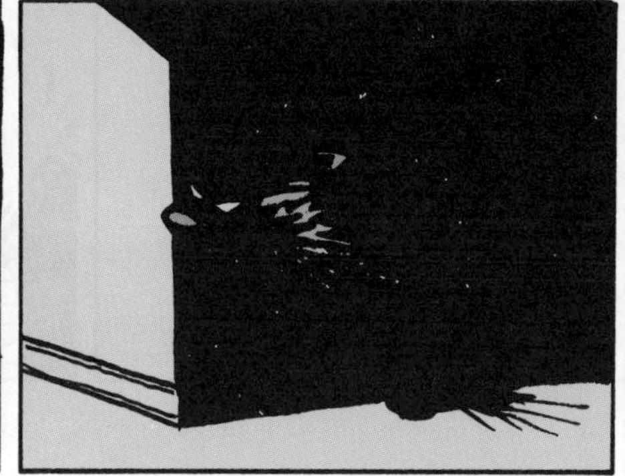

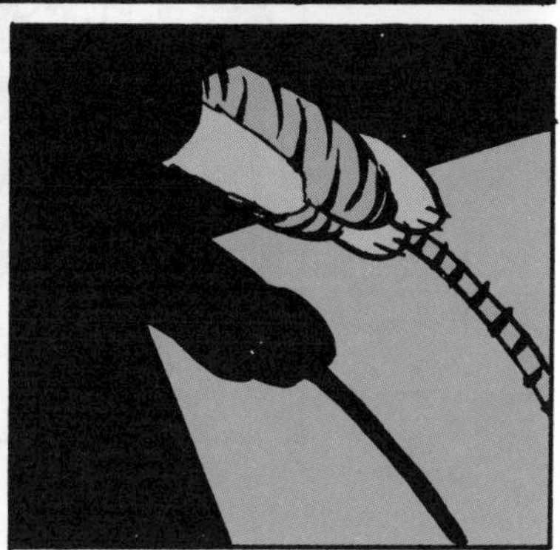

HERE, CALVIN, YOU GOT A LETTER IN THE MAIL.
I DID??

GOSH, I NEVER GET MAIL! I WONDER WHO SENT THIS. THERE'S NO RETURN ADDRESS!

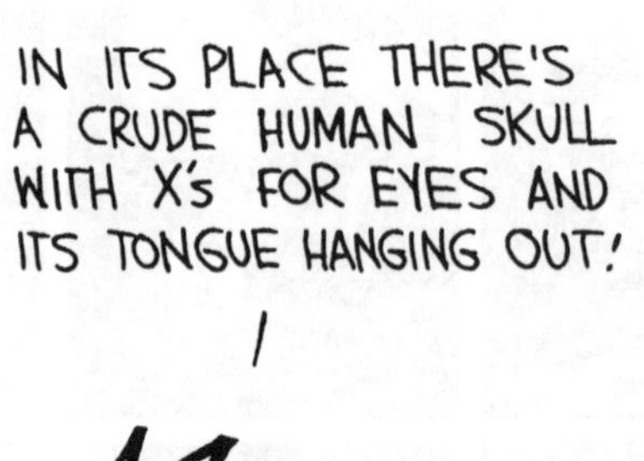
IN ITS PLACE THERE'S A CRUDE HUMAN SKULL WITH X's FOR EYES AND ITS TONGUE HANGING OUT!

MAYBE IT'S THE IRS.

LOOK, HOBBES, I GOT A MYSTERIOUS LETTER! THE RETURN ADDRESS IS A SKULL WITH X-ED OUT EYES!

IT HAS A LOCAL POSTMARK, THOUGH, SO I MUST KNOW THE PERSON.
OH BOY, INTRIGUE!

BUT WHO WOULD SEND ME AN ANONYMOUS, WEIRD LETTER LIKE THIS?
MAYBE A GIRL!

GAAAA! DOESN'T THE POST OFFICE SCREEN ANYTHING?!
I'LL GET YOU SOME GLOVES!

IF THIS IS FROM A GIRL, WE'LL HAVE TO BURY IT REAL DEEP AND DISINFECT MY ROOM.
HURRY! OPEN IT!

UGH, WHAT IF IT'S SOME MUSHY POEM WRITTEN WITH A PINK PEN IN LOOPY LETTERS WITH THE "I"S DOTTED WITH HEARTS ?? I THINK I'D PUKE.

NO, IT'S CUT AND PASTED LETTERS FROM A MAGAZINE!
WOW! NO HANDWRITING TO TRACE!

IT SAYS, "CODED MESSAGE TO FOLLOW. A=1, B=2, ETC. DESTROY THIS LETTER."
HOBBES, WE'RE DEALING WITH A **PRO**!

CAN YOU BELIEVE THIS?? A SKULL FOR A RETURN ADDRESS, UNTRACEABLE CUT-OUT LETTERS, AND A CODE KEY FOR A FUTURE MESSAGE!

THIS IS REAL SECRET AGENT STUFF! WHOEVER SENT THIS IS TAKING NO CHANCES ON THE MESSAGE BEING TRACED OR INTERCEPTED!

GOSH, THE MESSAGE MUST BE SUPER TOP SECRET AND IMPORTANT! I WONDER WHAT IT COULD BE! I WONDER WHEN I'LL FIND OUT!

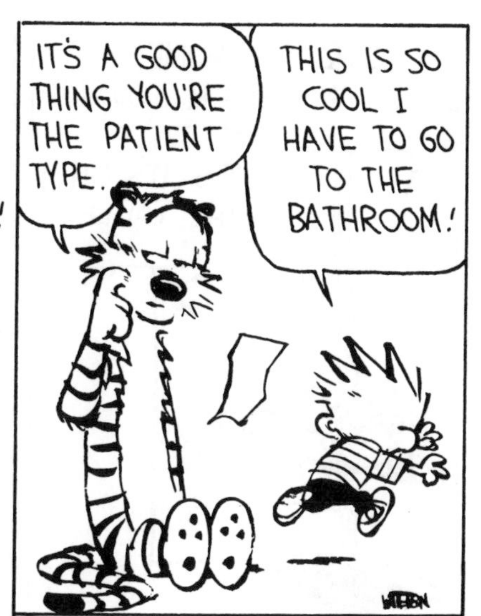
IT'S A GOOD THING YOU'RE THE PATIENT TYPE.
THIS IS SO COOL I HAVE TO GO TO THE BATHROOM!

THIS IS SO EXCITING TO GET A SECRET UNTRACEABLE MESSAGE IN THE MAIL!

IT SAID A CODED LETTER WOULD FOLLOW! MAYBE IT WILL ARRIVE TODAY! I CAN'T WAIT TO GET HOME AND SEE!

I WONDER WHAT IT WILL SAY? I WONDER WHO SENT IT? I WONDER WHY IT'S IN CODE?

I'LL BET I GROW UP TO BE A SPY! I'M SO GOOD AT FIGURING OUT WHAT'S GOING ON!
WATTERSON

I'M HOME! I'M HOME! DID I GET A LETTER TODAY??
YES, IT'S ON THE TABLE.

OH BOY, HOBBES, THIS IS IT! THIS IS THE CODED MESSAGE!
QUICK, LET'S DECIPHER IT!

OK, THE FIRST NUMBER IS 3, SO THAT WOULD BE "C". NEXT IS 1, SO THAT'S "A."
THIS IS FUN!

HEY! THIS SAYS, "CALVIN IS A PORRIDGE BRAIN!" IT'S... IT'S AN **INSULT**!
SOME PEOPLE HAVE SECRET ADMIRERS. **YOU** HAVE A SECRET DETRACTOR!
WATTERSON

OOH, THIS BURNS ME UP! A CODED MESSAGE SAYING "CALVIN IS A PORRIDGE BRAIN!" THE NERVE!

THE BIZARRE SKULL DRAWING, THE CUT AND PASTED LETTERS, THE CODE... ALL THAT SUSPENSE AND MYSTERY FOR AN INSULT!

WHAT KIND OF DEPRAVED MANIAC WOULD GO TO SO MUCH TROUBLE?! RRRGHH, I WISH I KNEW WHO SENT THIS!!

OUR ONLY CLUE IS THAT THE TWISTED FIEND HAS TOO MUCH TIME ON HIS HANDS.
ANOTHER LETTER FOR YOU, CALVIN! HOW NICE TO GET SO MUCH MAIL.
WATERSON

LOOK, HOBBES, THE SKULL! IT'S ANOTHER LETTER FROM THE SECRET INSULTER!

MORE CUT AND PASTED LETTERS! IT SAYS, "YOU LOOK LIKE A BABOON AND YOU SMELL LIKE ONE TOO! HA HA."

THE MYSTERY DEEPENS.
WHO COULD BE SENDING THESE?!

A RECKLESS EXAGGERATOR. YOU DON'T *LOOK* LIKE A BABOON.
OH, YOU'RE A *BIG* HELP!
WATERSON

I CAN'T SLEEP.

WHO'S BEEN SENDING ME THESE INSULTS?! WHERE WILL IT STOP?! AM I GOING TO GET AN INSULT IN THE MAIL EVERY DAY FOR THE REST OF MY LIFE??

THE THING THAT DRIVES ME CRAZY IS THERE'S NO WAY TO TRACE THIS LUNATIC! HE'S THOUGHT OF EVERYTHING! HE'S A MASTERMIND!

HEY, WHO CUT UP MY MAGAZINE?

DID I GET ANOTHER LETTER TODAY?
YEP! WHEN YOU WRITE TO YOURSELF, YOU GET A LOT OF MAIL.

I DON'T WRITE THESE! WHAT ARE YOU TALKING ABOUT?
OH C'MON, CALVIN. I KNOW YOU'VE BEEN PUTTING THESE OUT FOR THE MAILMAN EVERY DAY.

WAIT A MINUTE! THESE ARE COMING FROM **OUR** HOUSE??
OH, AND I WANT YOU TO **ASK** BEFORE YOU CUT UP MY MAGAZINES, OK?

ALL RIGHT, WHERE'S THAT MISERABLE BUNCH OF STRIPEY ORANGE FLEA BAIT?!?

SO IT WAS **YOU** THE WHOLE TIME! **YOU'RE** THE ONE WHO'S BEEN SENDING ME INSULTS IN THE MAIL!!

I'LL GET YOU FOR THIS! YOU AND YOUR SNEAKY CODES AND PASTED LETTERS AND SKULL DRAWINGS!

..ALTHOUGH, REALLY, THE SKULL DRAWINGS WERE PRETTY COOL.
YOU CAN TELL A GOOD SPY BY HIS OMINOUS LOGO.

YOU AND I ARE THROUGH! I'LL TEACH YOU TO TRICK ME, YOU BIG HAIRBALL!
YOU JUST HAVE NO SENSE OF HUMOR!

I DO TOO! IT'S JUST THAT WAS A TERRIBLE, NASTY, AWFUL THING TO DO, AND I'LL NEVER FORGIV.. HUH?

HEYYYYY, YOU'RE RIGHT! IT ***IS*** FUNNY! HA HA HA! ..OK! WE'RE PALS AGAIN!

SUSIE:
you Smell!
HA ha!

SOME NOVEMBER *THIS* IS.

THE LEAVES ARE DOWN BUT THERE'S NO SNOW.

Calvin and HOBBES
by WATTERSON
EVERYTHING IS JUST SITTING AROUND WAITING FOR WINTER, BUT NOTHING IS HAPPENING.

C'MON, WHAT'S THE **BIG** HOLDUP?!' LET'S **GO**, UP THERE! BRING ON THE **SNOW**!

SIGHH
NO EFFICIENCY. NO ACCOUNTABILITY. I TELL YOU, HOBBES, IT'S A LOUSY WAY TO RUN A UNIVERSE.
WHATEVER HAPPENED TO THE WORK ETHIC?

...MEETING SMILE AFTER SA-MI-I-ILE. IN THE AIR THERE'S A FEE-HEELING OF CHRISTMASSS...

NOT THINKING ABOUT IT WON'T MAKE IT GO AWAY, YOU KNOW!

LOOK HOBBES, I GOT A PAINT-BY-NUMBERS KIT! IT'S REALLY FUN.

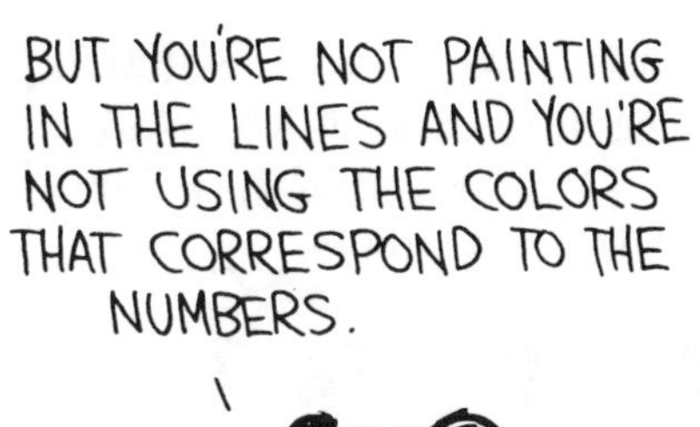
BUT YOU'RE NOT PAINTING IN THE LINES AND YOU'RE NOT USING THE COLORS THAT CORRESPOND TO THE NUMBERS.

IF I DID ***THAT***, I'D GET THE PICTURE THEY SHOW ON THE BOX!
AH.

WELL, YOUR HAIRCUT IS A BIG IMPROVEMENT.

YOU **LIKE** WHAT IT SAYS ON THE BACK OF MY HEAD?
WHAT **WHAT** SAYS?

DIDN'T THE BARBER SHAVE, "I MAY HAVE A BAD HAIRCUT, BUT YOU'RE DOWNRIGHT UGLY," BACK THERE?!
GOOD HEAVENS, NO!

OK, CHARLIE, GIMME BACK THAT TIP!

THESE FALL MORNINGS SURE ARE PRETTY. THE BRISK AIR, THE SMELL OF LEAVES...

...ALL RUINED BECAUSE I HAVE TO GET ON A BUS AND GO TO SCHOOL.

WHEN I WAS A PRE-SCHOOLER, I NEVER TOOK ADVANTAGE OF FALL MORNINGS. I DIDN'T APPRECIATE THEM.

ANOTHER SQUANDERED YOUTH.
SIGHHH... I WAS SO YOUNG AND FOOLISH. I THOUGHT THOSE DAYS WOULD LAST FOREVER.

HELLO? ... NO, MY MOM CAN'T COME TO THE PHONE RIGHT NOW.

SURE, I'D BE GLAD TO TAKE A MESSAGE.

YOU WRITE IT DOWN, DRIVE IT OVER HERE, PAY ME FIVE BUCKS, AND I'LL GIVE IT TO HER THE NEXT TIME I SEE HER.

HE MUST NOT HAVE WANTED TO TALK TO MOM VERY BAD.

I'M GROWING MY FINGERNAILS LONG.

THEN I'LL FILE THEM INTO POINTS, SO I'LL HAVE CLAWS JUST LIKE YOU.

MINE ARE RETRACTABLE.

NO RETRACTABLE CLAWS, NO OPPOSABLE TOES, NO PREHENSILE TAIL, NO COMPOUND EYES, NO FANGS, NO WINGS..
..SIGHHH...

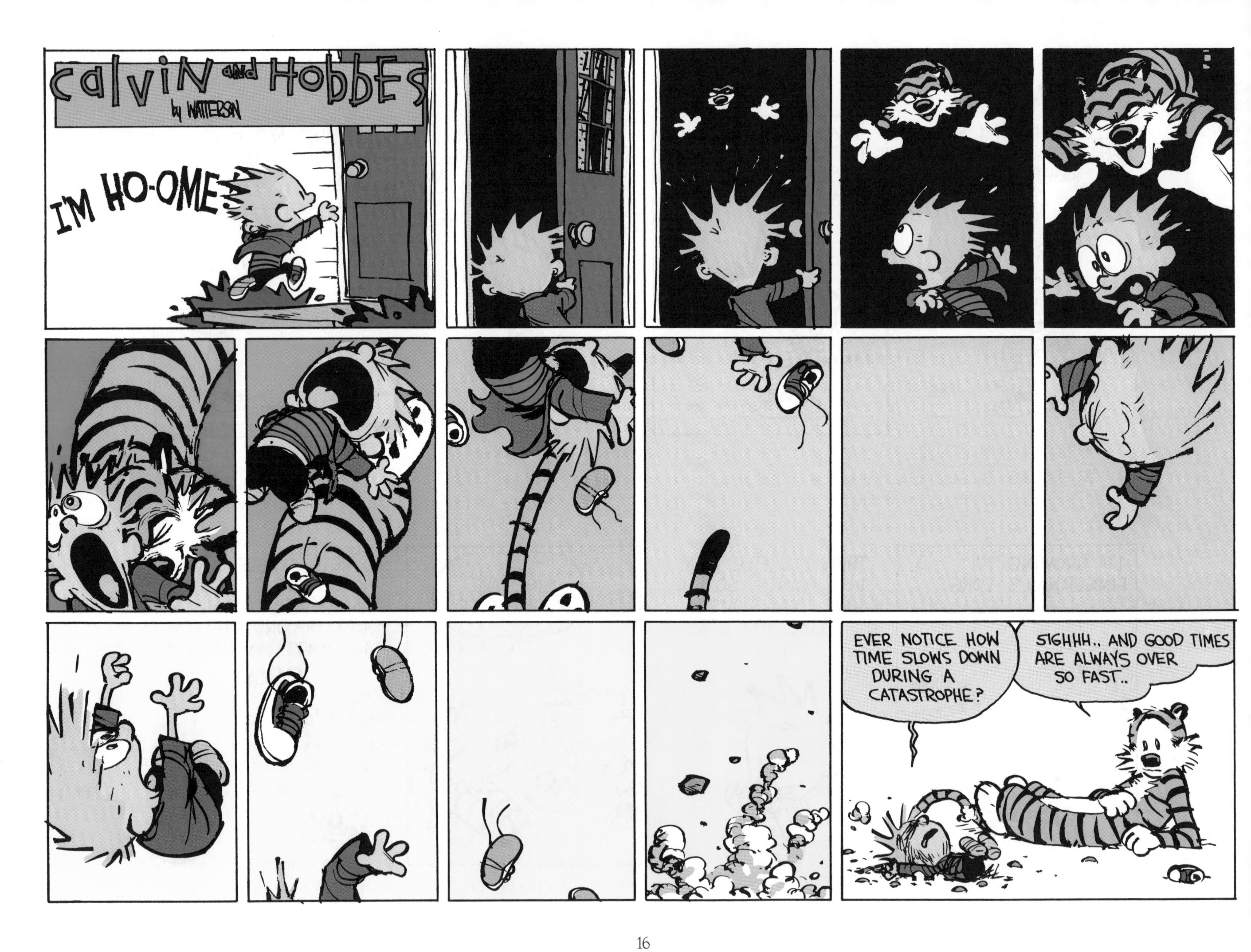
Calvin and Hobbes
by WATTERSON
I'M HO-OME
EVER NOTICE HOW TIME SLOWS DOWN DURING A CATASTROPHE?
SIGHHH.. AND GOOD TIMES ARE ALWAYS OVER SO FAST..

CAN I LEARN TO PARACHUTE OUT OF AN AIRPLANE?

WHY DON'T YOU JUST PLAY "CHICKEN" ON THE RAILROAD TRACKS? IT WOULD BE A CHEAPER WAY TO TOY WITH DEATH, I'M SURE.

MOM'S SO PRACTICAL.

THIS CONNECT-THE-DOTS BOOK REALLY MAKES ME MAD! LOOK AT THIS.

IT'S A DUCK.
I KNOW! WHO WANTS TO DRAW A DUCK?! I SURE DIDN'T! THEY MADE ME!

I'VE BEEN MANIPULATED! MY NATURAL ARTISTIC TALENT HAS BEEN USED AGAINST MY WILL TO CREATE SOME CORPORATE ENTITY'S CRUDE IDEA OF WATERFOWL! IT'S OUTRAGEOUS!

ANOTHER BLOW TO CREATIVE INTEGRITY.
FROM NOW ON, I'LL CONNECT THE DOTS MY OWN WAY.

MISS WORMWOOD, MY DAD SAYS WHEN HE WAS IN SCHOOL, THEY TAUGHT HIM TO DO MATH ON A SLIDE RULE.

HE SAYS HE HASN'T USED A SLIDE RULE SINCE, BECAUSE HE GOT A FIVE-BUCK CALCULATOR THAT CAN DO MORE FUNCTIONS THAN HE COULD FIGURE OUT IF HIS LIFE DEPENDED ON IT.

GIVEN THE PACE OF TECHNOLOGY, I PROPOSE WE LEAVE MATH TO THE MACHINES AND GO PLAY OUTSIDE.

MY BILLS ALWAYS DIE IN SUBCOMMITTEE.

HOW DO BANK MACHINES WORK?
BANK

WELL, LET'S SAY YOU WANT 25 DOLLARS. YOU PUNCH IN THE AMOUNT...

..AND BEHIND THE MACHINE THERE'S A GUY WITH A PRINTING PRESS WHO MAKES THE MONEY AND STICKS IT OUT THIS SLOT.

SORT OF LIKE THE GUY WHO LIVES UP IN OUR GARAGE AND OPENS THE DOOR?
EXACTLY.

MISS WORMWOOD?
YES, CALVIN?

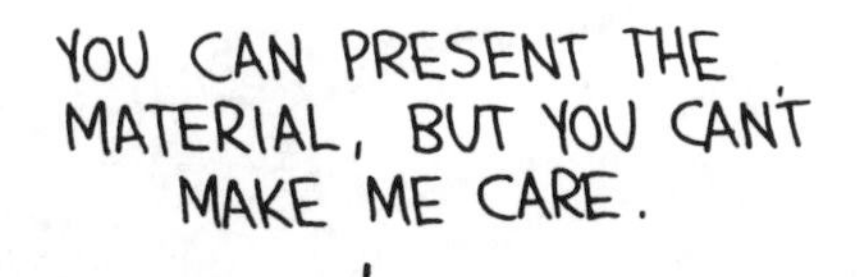
YOU CAN PRESENT THE MATERIAL, BUT YOU CAN'T MAKE ME CARE.

RUMOR HAS IT SHE'S UP TO TWO PACKS A DAY, UNFILTERED.

I'VE NOTICED THAT COMIC BOOK SUPERHEROES USUALLY FIGHT EVIL MANIACS WITH GRANDIOSE PLANS TO DESTROY THE WORLD.

WHY DON'T SUPERHEROES GO AFTER MORE SUBTLE, REALISTIC BAD GUYS?

YEAH, THE SUPERHERO COULD ATTEND COUNCIL MEETINGS AND WRITE LETTERS TO THE EDITOR, AND STUFF.

HMM... I THINK I SEE THE PROBLEM.
"QUICK! TO THE BAT-FAX!"

Calvin and Hobbes

by WATTERSON

SCREAMING, SUSIE HURLS HERSELF TOWARD THE SCHOOL DOORS, BUT THE PACK IS CLOSING IN!

THANK YOU FOR THAT TASTELESS AND ENTIRELY UNINFORMATIVE REPORT ON OVERPOPULATION. SEE ME AFTER CLASS.

YA LIKE THAT, SUSIE??

SUSIE, CAN I COPY YOUR ANSWERS?
HECK NO!

WHY NOT?
BECAUSE YOU'D GET A GOOD GRADE WITHOUT DOING ANY WORK.

SO?
SO IT'S WRONG TO GET REWARDS YOU HAVEN'T EARNED.

I'VE NEVER HEARD OF ANYONE WHO COULDN'T LIVE WITH THAT.

FOR "SHOW AND TELL" TODAY, I DON'T HAVE ANYTHING TO SHOW.

BUT I'LL TELL YOU THAT, WHEN I'M AT SCHOOL, MY MOM PUTS ON A PATRIOTIC LEOTARD, A CAPE, AND KNEE-HIGH, HIGH-HEELED BOOTS, AND SHE FIGHTS CRIME AS A SUPER HEROINE.

I HOPE YOU'RE ALL DULY IMPRESSED. THANK YOU VERY MUCH.

THAT'S THE NOTE HIS TEACHER SENT HOME WITH HIM.
WOW, SHOW ME THAT OUTFIT SOMETIME.

DO YOU HATE BEING A GIRL?
IT'S GOTTA BE BETTER THAN THE ALTERNATIVE.

WHAT'S IT LIKE? IS IT LIKE BEING A BUG?
LIKE A *WHAT?!*

I IMAGINE BUGS AND GIRLS HAVE A DIM PERCEPTION THAT NATURE PLAYED A CRUEL TRICK ON THEM, BUT THEY LACK THE INTELLIGENCE TO REALLY COMPREHEND THE MAGNITUDE OF IT.

I MUST'VE PUT MY FINGER ON IT.
WATERSON

I'M HOME! I'M FREE! THE REST OF THE DAY IS ALL MINE!
OLS
WATERSON

FINALLY, SOME TIME TO MYSELF! LIBERTY, PRECIOUS LIBERTY! HA HA HA!

DAD, ARE YOU VICARIOUSLY LIVING THROUGH ME IN THE HOPE THAT MY ACCOMPLISHMENTS WILL VALIDATE YOUR MEDIOCRE LIFE AND IN SOME WAY COMPENSATE FOR ALL OF THE OPPORTUNITIES YOU BOTCHED?

IF I WERE, YOU CAN BET I'D BE RE-EVALUATING MY STRATEGY.

MOM, DAD KEEPS INSULTING ME.

I LIKE ROCKS. HERE'S A NICE ONE.

SEE HOW SMOOTH IT IS? IT PROBABLY TOOK EONS TO GET LIKE THAT.

IT'S A SEDIMENTARY ROCK, FORMED BY SEDIMENT DEPOSITS, AS OPPOSED TO, SAY, AN IGNEOUS ROCK, WHICH IS VOLCANIC IN ORIGIN.

YOU SURE KNOW A LOT ABOUT ROCKS.
YOU BET. BALLISTIC MISSILES FROM GOD, I CALL 'EM.

Calvin and HOBBES
by WATTERSON

COOKI
MATH

Dear Santa,
This Year, I don't want any Gifts. I just want Love and Peace for my fellow man.

I'M GUESSING CHEAP ELF LABOR, LOWER ENVIRONMENTAL STANDARDS, AND TAX BREAKS. IS THIS REALLY THE EXAMPLE YOU WANT TO SET FOR US IMPRESSIONABLE KIDS?

DEAR SANTA,
LAST YEAR I ASKED FOR A LONG-RANGE THERMO-NUCLEAR "SMART" MISSILE AND A LAUNCHER.

INSTEAD, I GOT SOCKS AND A SHIRT. OBVIOUSLY, YOU MIXED UP MY ORDER WITH SOMEONE ELSE'S.

LET'S GET WITH THE PROGRAM, HUH?

JUST BECAUSE HE GIVES THE STUFF AWAY FREE, HE THINKS HE CAN GET AWAY WITH AN INCOMPETENT ORGANIZATION.

LOOK AT THIS GREAT SNOWBALL! I'D SURE LIKE TO PASTE SOMEONE UPSIDE THE HEAD WITH IT.

...BUT I FIGURE EACH SNOWBALL I THROW MEANS I'LL GET ONE LESS PRESENT FROM SANTA.

I WISH I KNEW IF SANTA WAS BRINGING ME ANY UNDERWEAR.

SKI RESORTS USE MAN-MADE SNOW.

THEY HAVE SNOW-MAKING MACHINES THAT CAN COVER A WHOLE HILLSIDE.

HINT, HINT.
YOU CAN RELY ON THE WEATHER LIKE EVERY OTHER KID.

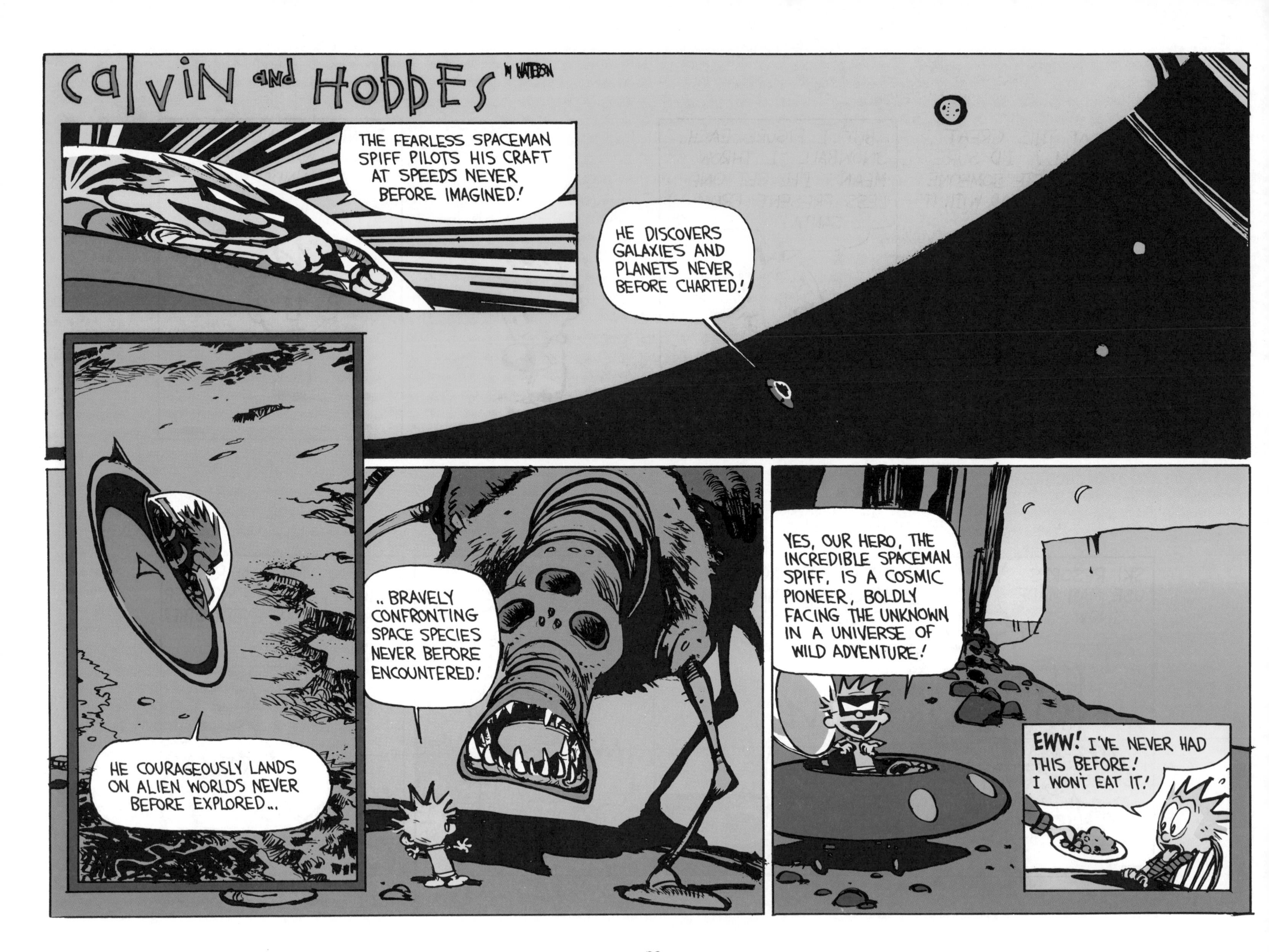
Calvin and Hobbes
THE FEARLESS SPACEMAN SPIFF PILOTS HIS CRAFT AT SPEEDS NEVER BEFORE IMAGINED!
HE DISCOVERS GALAXIES AND PLANETS NEVER BEFORE CHARTED!
HE COURAGEOUSLY LANDS ON ALIEN WORLDS NEVER BEFORE EXPLORED...
.. BRAVELY CONFRONTING SPACE SPECIES NEVER BEFORE ENCOUNTERED!
YES, OUR HERO, THE INCREDIBLE SPACEMAN SPIFF, IS A COSMIC PIONEER, BOLDLY FACING THE UNKNOWN IN A UNIVERSE OF WILD ADVENTURE!
EWW! I'VE NEVER HAD THIS BEFORE! I WON'T EAT IT!

OH LOOK, YET ANOTHER CHRISTMAS TV SPECIAL!

HOW TOUCHING TO HAVE THE MEANING OF CHRISTMAS BROUGHT TO US BY COLA, FAST FOOD, AND BEER CONGLOMERATES.

WHO'D HAVE EVER GUESSED PRODUCT CONSUMPTION, POPULAR ENTERTAINMENT, AND SPIRITUALITY WOULD MIX SO HARMONIOUSLY.
IT'S A BEAUTIFUL WORLD, ALL RIGHT.

DAD DOESN'T HANDLE THE SEASON'S STRESS VERY GRACEFULLY.

DAD, I'D LIKE TO HAVE A LITTLE TALK.
UM, OK...

AS THE WAGE EARNER HERE, IT'S YOUR RESPONSIBILITY TO SHOW SOME CONSUMER CONFIDENCE AND START BUYING THINGS THAT WILL GET THE ECONOMY GOING AND CREATE PROFITS AND EMPLOYMENT.

HERE'S A LIST OF SOME BIG-TICKET ITEMS I'D LIKE FOR CHRISTMAS. I HOPE I CAN TRUST YOU TO DO WHAT'S RIGHT FOR OUR COUNTRY.

I'VE GOT TO STOP LEAVING THE WALL STREET JOURNAL AROUND.

Calvin and Hobbes
by WATTERSON
I WISH SANTA WOULD PUBLISH THE GUIDELINES HE USES FOR DETERMINING A KID'S GOODNESS.

FOR EXAMPLE, HOW MUCH DOES HE WEIGH MOTIVES? DOES HE CONSIDER THE KID'S NATURAL PREDISPOSITION?

I MEAN, IF SOME SICKENINGLY WHOLESOME NERD *LIKES* BEING GOOD, IT'S *EASY* FOR HIM TO MEET THE STANDARDS! THERE'S NO CHALLENGE!
HECK, ANYONE CAN BE GOOD IF HE *WANTS* TO BE! THE TRUE TEST OF ONE'S METTLE IS BEING GOOD WHEN ONE HAS AN INNATE INCLINATION TOWARDS EVIL.

I THINK ONE GOOD ACT BY *ME*, EVEN IF IT'S JUST TO GET PRESENTS, SHOULD COUNT AS *FIVE* GOOD ACTS BY SOME SWEET-TEMPERED KID MOTIVATED BY THE PURENESS OF HIS HEART, DON'T YOU?
HEY SUSIE!
POW!
OF COURSE, IN YOUR CASE, THE QUESTION IS ACADEMIC.
I WANTED TO PUT A ROCK IN THE SNOWBALL, BUT I DIDN'T! THAT SHOULD BE WORTH A LOT!

RRRRGGHHH

I SAY, IF A NOVELTY CHRISTMAS SONG IS FUNNY THE FIRST TIME, IT'S FUNNY **EVERY** TIME.

I'M HAVING A LOT OF HOLIDAY STRESS.

WHY? YOU DON'T SHOP FOR ANYONE, YOU'VE GOT TWO WEEKS OFF FROM SCHOOL, AND YOUR PARENTS DO ALL THE COOKING, CLEANING, AND DECORATING!
HOW COULD YOU HAVE HOLIDAY STRESS?

DEEP DOWN, I DOUBT MY GREED FOR PRESENTS CAN OVERCOME MY DESIRE TO MISBEHAVE.

OK HOBBES, I'VE GOT A PLAN.
YEAH?

IF I DO TEN SPONTANEOUS ACTS OF GOOD WILL A DAY FROM NOW UNTIL CHRISTMAS, SANTA WILL HAVE TO BE LENIENT IN JUDGING THE REST OF THIS LAST YEAR! I CAN CLAIM I'VE TURNED A NEW LEAF!

TEN SPONTANEOUS ACTS OF GOOD WILL A DAY? THAT'S PRETTY MANY.
DON'T REMIND ME.

WELL, HERE'S YOUR CHANCE. SUSIE'S COMING THIS WAY.
MAYBE I'LL START TOMORROW AND DO **20** A DAY.

OH MAN, SUSIE'S RIGHT IN RANGE! IT'S A CLEAR SHOT! I CAN'T MISS!
I THOUGHT YOU WERE GOING TO DO TEN SPONTANEOUS ACTS OF GOOD WILL A DAY.
IT'S NOT EVEN NOON. I'LL DO 'EM AFTER LUNCH.

LOOK, DOING TEN GOOD ACTS ISN'T GOING TO IMPRESS SANTA IF YOU DO **BAD** THINGS ALL MORNING!

SUPPOSE I JUST GRAZE HER JAW AND KNOCK SOME FILLINGS LOOSE. THAT WOULD BE IN THE GRAY AREA, DON'T YOU THINK?
DON'T EXPECT TO PLAY WITH ALL **MY** PRESENTS WHEN YOU DON'T GET ANY.

JUST MAKE SURE YOUR HANDS ARE CLEAN AND ACID-FREE, AND ONLY TOUCH THE MYLAR BAG, AND USE THESE STERILIZED TONGS TO TURN THE PAGES, AND TRY NOT TO EXHALE TOO MUCH MOISTURE, OK?! DON'T MESS IT UP!

MUSH
HULLP
SMACK

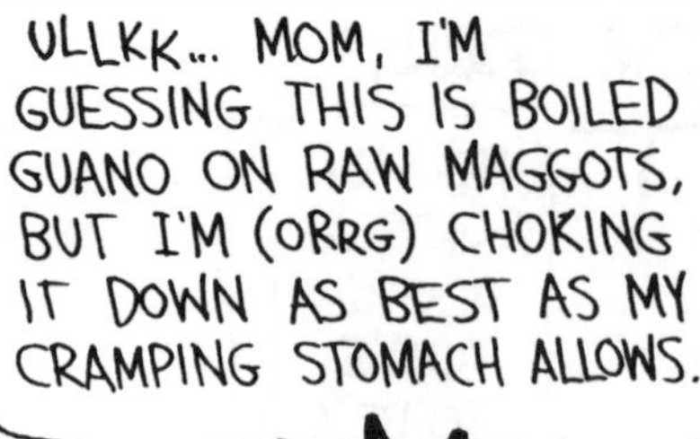
ULLKK... MOM, I'M GUESSING THIS IS BOILED GUANO ON RAW MAGGOTS, BUT I'M (ORRG) CHOKING IT DOWN AS BEST AS MY CRAMPING STOMACH ALLOWS.

THIS IS ANOTHER SPONTANEOUS ACT OF GOOD WILL, SANTA! YOU'D BETTER COME THROUGH IN SPADES FOR THIS!!

MORE MAGGOTS?
SURE! PILE 'EM ON!

ONE MORE DAY OF BEING GOOD! THIS HAS BEEN THE LONGEST WEEK OF MY ENTIRE LIFE.

HEY! I'LL BET SANTA'S LOADING UP THE SLEIGH RIGHT NOW! HE'S GOT MILLIONS OF DELIVERIES, RIGHT? HE COULDN'T POSSIBLY STILL BE DECIDING HOW GOOD I AM!

IF HIS DECISION IS MADE, I DON'T HAVE TO IMPRESS HIM ANY MORE! I'M FREE! THE CHARADE IS OVER! I CAN DO WHAT I WANT!

MAYBE HE'S LOADING YOUR STUFF LAST, JUST TO SEE WHAT YOU DO.
YOU THINK? WELL, MAYBE. GEEZ, HE'S A TOUGH OL' GEEZER! WELL, WHAT'S ONE MORE DAY? .. SIGH...

IT'S A CERTIFICATE ENTITLING THE BEARER TO ONE DAY POUNCE-FREE OF TIGER ATTACKS! WOW! THANKS, OL' BUDDY! YOU ALWAYS THINK OF THE BEST GIFTS!
I STILL THINK THIS COULD'VE WAITED UNTIL SUNRISE.
SHH, TAKE A PICTURE.

THE SNOW ISN'T DEEP ENOUGH FOR SLEDDING.

AND IT'S NOT WET ENOUGH TO PACK, EITHER.

SIGHHHH

FORTUNATELY, I'M THE STOIC TYPE.
YOU'RE AN INSPIRATION TO US ALL.

Calvin and Hobbes
by WATTERSON
EVERYBODY MAKES THE WRONG KIND OF NEW YEAR'S RESOLUTION.
ALL THEY DO IS PROMISE TO STOP BAD HABITS AND START GOOD HABITS.
WHAT'S WRONG WITH THAT?
IT'S NOT ENOUGH TO CHANGE A FEW LITTLE HABITS! EVERYBODY I KNOW NEEDS A COMPLETE PERSONALITY OVERHAUL!
THAT'S WHY I'LL BE SPENDING THE REMAINING DAYS OF THIS YEAR TELLING PEOPLE WHAT I HATE ABOUT THEM AND HOW THEY SHOULD CHANGE.
SOME OF US WOULD BE HAPPY TO RECIPROCATE.
SORRY. MY NEW YEAR'S RESOLUTION IS NOT TO CHANGE A BIT.

YOU KNOW, IT'S AMAZING HOW MANY THINGS YOU CAN TAKE APART WITH JUST ONE ORDINARY SCREWDRIVER!

SUCH AS?
WELL, JUST FOR STARTERS, THERE'S...

...THAT IS, HYPOTHETICALLY, I MEAN ... NOT THAT I'D KNOW FOR A FACT, OF COURSE... JUST IN THEORY, I IMAGINE THAT MAYBE... UM, WELL, GOSH, IT'S HARD TO SAY.

I'VE **GOT** TO STOP INTRODUCING TOPICS OF CONVERSATION.

YOU KNOW WHAT THE PROBLEM IS WITH THE UNIVERSE?
UM...

THERE'S NO TOLL-FREE CUSTOMER SERVICE HOT LINE FOR COMPLAINTS! THAT'S WHY THINGS DON'T GET FIXED!

IF THE UNIVERSE HAD ANY DECENT MANAGEMENT, WE'D GET A FULL REFUND IF WE WEREN'T COMPLETELY SATISFIED!

BUT THE PLACE IS FREE.
SEE, THAT'S ANOTHER THING. THEY SHOULD HAVE A COVER CHARGE AND KEEP OUT THE RIFFRAFF.

DO YOU NEED NAILS POUNDED INTO ANYTHING? YOU NAME THE SURFACE AND I'LL FILL IT FULL OF NAILS!
UM, NO...

YOU SURE? I'VE GOT THE TOOLS RIGHT HERE! LOTS OF NAIL SIZES! I'D BE HAPPY TO DO IT!
NO THANKS, NOT TODAY.

OK, WELL, LET ME KNOW IF YOU CHANGE YOUR MIND.

MM-HMM.
MOM WANTED A GIRL. I JUST KNOW IT.
DID SHE NEED ANYTHING SAWED?

PEOPLE ALWAYS SEEM SO CRABBY AND ANIMALS ALWAYS SEEM SO CONTENT. I WONDER WHY THAT IS.

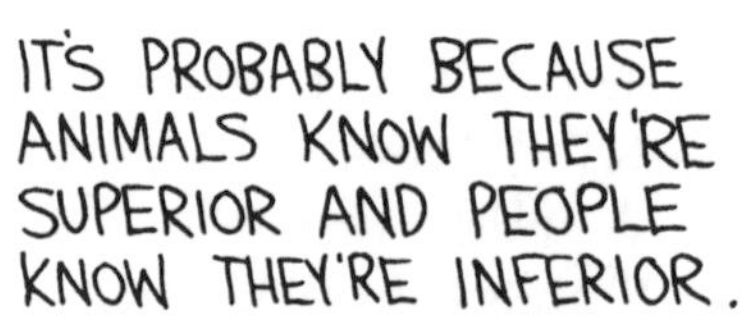
IT'S PROBABLY BECAUSE ANIMALS KNOW THEY'RE SUPERIOR AND PEOPLE KNOW THEY'RE INFERIOR.

I FIGURED IT WAS BECAUSE ANIMALS GET 15 HOURS OF SLEEP EVERY DAY.

ACTUALLY, I THINK ANIMALS ARE JUST AS CRABBY AS PEOPLE ARE.

WOW, LOOK AT THE SNOW COMING DOWN! THE ROADS ARE A MESS!

I HOPE DAD MAKES IT HOME OK.

FACE IT, DAD. THE SEASON'S **OVER**.
ARE YOU KIDDING? IN THIS STUFF, I REACH MY OPTIMAL HEART RATE IN NO TIME!

I'VE DECIDED TO STOP CARING ABOUT THINGS.

IF YOU CARE, YOU JUST GET DISAPPOINTED ALL THE TIME. IF YOU **DON'T** CARE, NOTHING MATTERS, SO YOU'RE NEVER UPSET.

FROM NOW ON, MY RALLYING CRY IS, "**SO WHAT?!**"

THAT'S A TOUGH CRY TO RALLY AROUND.
SO WHAT?!

IT'S A NEW YEAR... A NEW BEGINNING! NEW POSSIBILITIES!
THIS SNOWMAN REPRESENTS THE SPIRIT OF THE NEW YEAR.
LOOKING AHEAD, HE STRIDES FORWARD WITH CONFIDENCE AND DETERMINATION!
HE CHALLENGES! HE IMAGINES! HE INVENTS! HE CALLS FORTH THE BEST QUALITIES OF HUMAN DRIVE AND INGENUITY!
calvin and HOBBES by WATTERSON
VERY INSPIRING.
THANK YOU.
...AND OVER HERE IS THE REAL WORLD?
RIGHT. THIS IS WHY WE'RE ALWAYS GLAD WHEN THE OLD YEAR IS OVER.

I'M NOT GETTING UP UNTIL IT'S AS WARM OUT THERE AS IT IS IN HERE.

I DON'T WANT TO GO TO SCHOOL. I DON'T WANT TO KNOW ANYTHING NEW.

I ALREADY KNOW MORE THAN I WANT TO! I LIKED THINGS BETTER WHEN I DIDN'T UNDERSTAND THEM!

THE FACT IS, I'M BEING EDUCATED AGAINST MY WILL! MY RIGHTS ARE BEING TRAMPLED!

IS IT A RIGHT TO REMAIN IGNORANT?
I DON'T KNOW, BUT I REFUSE TO FIND OUT!

IT WOULD SURE BE A BIG SURPRISE IF THE SCHOOL BUS SPONTANEOUSLY EXPLODED AND I DIDN'T HAVE TO GO TO SCHOOL!

YEAH, I'D SURE BE SURPRISED IF **THAT** HAPPENED!

LIFE IS FULL OF SURPRISES, BUT NEVER WHEN YOU NEED ONE.
ARY SCHOOL

I'M HO-OME!

HELLO??

THANKS FOR THE BIG WELCOME!
YOU'RE LETTING IN COLD AIR.

PROBLEMS OFTEN LOOK OVERWHELMING AT FIRST.

THE SECRET IS TO BREAK PROBLEMS INTO SMALL, MANAGEABLE CHUNKS. IF YOU DEAL WITH THOSE, YOU'RE DONE BEFORE YOU KNOW IT.

FOR EXAMPLE, I'M SUPPOSED TO READ THIS ENTIRE HISTORY CHAPTER. IT LOOKS IMPOSSIBLE, SO I BREAK THE PROBLEM DOWN.

YOU FOCUS ON READING THE FIRST SECTION?
I ASK MYSELF, "DO I EVEN CARE?"
WATTERSON

WHATCHA DOIN'?
I'M KILLING TIME WHILE I WAIT FOR LIFE TO SHOWER ME WITH MEANING AND HAPPINESS.

I HOPE YOU'RE COMFY.
YOU COULD GET ME SOMETHING TO EAT.

Calvin and HOBBES by WATTERSON
THIS IS MY LATEST SNOW SCULPTURE.
WHERE?
ALL OF THIS!
BUT YOU DIDN'T DO ANYTHING.
RIGHT. ART IS DEAD! THERE'S NOTHING LEFT TO SAY. STYLE IS EXHAUSTED AND CONTENT IS POINTLESS. ART HAS NO PURPOSE. ALL THAT'S LEFT IS COMMODITY MARKETING.
CONSEQUENTLY, I'M SIGNING THIS LANDSCAPE, AND YOU CAN OWN IT FOR A MILLION DOLLARS.
CALV
SORRY....IT DOESN'T MATCH MY FURNITURE.
THE PROBLEM WITH BEING AVANT-GARDE IS KNOWING WHO'S PUTTING ON WHO.

THIS SNOWMAN DOESN'T LOOK VERY HAPPY.
HE'S NOT.

HE KNOWS IT'S JUST A MATTER OF TIME BEFORE HE MELTS. THE SUN IGNORES HIS ENTREATIES. HE FEELS HIS EXISTENCE IS MEANINGLESS.

IS IT?
NOPE. HE'S ABOUT TO BUY A BIG SCREEN TV.

HOME, SWEET HOME.

FOR THE TOWNSFOLK BELOW, THE DAY BEGAN LIKE ANY OTHER DAY.

WHAT'S WRONG WITH YOUR SNOWMAN?!
IT'S A SNOW **WOMAN**.

I DON'T CARE. WE'RE NOT HAVING AN ANATOMICALLY CORRECT SNOWMAN IN THE FRONT YARD.

I HATE TRUDGING UP THESE HILLS.

I DIDN'T COME OUT HERE TO **WORK**! I CAME OUT HERE TO RIDE AND HAVE **FUN**!

WELL, YOU CAN'T RIDE THE SLED IF YOU DON'T CLIMB THE HILLS.
I COULD IF YOU PULLED ME UP.

HE'S SO LAZY AND SELFISH.

HA HA! I'D SURE LIKE TO SEE MOM MAKE ME COME INSIDE **NOW**!

WITH THIS FORT AND THIS ARSENAL OF 200 SNOWBALLS, **NOBODY** CAN TELL **ME** WHAT TO DO! I CAN STAY OUT HERE ALL DAY!

AT LAST, I'M THE MASTER OF MY FATE! I'LL STAY OUTSIDE AS LONG AS I PLEASE!

BACK INSIDE SO SOON?
IT'S TOO COLD OUT.

Calvin and Hobbes
by Watterson

EGGPLANT CASSEROLE TONIGHT?
WHY, YES!

ALL THAT FUR MUST BE STRICTLY ORNAMENTAL.

NICE TRYYY!

NOTHING I DO IS MY FAULT.

MY FAMILY IS DYSFUNCTIONAL AND MY PARENTS WON'T EMPOWER ME! CONSEQUENTLY, I'M NOT SELF-ACTUALIZED!

MY BEHAVIOR IS ADDICTIVE FUNCTIONING IN A DISEASE PROCESS OF TOXIC CODEPENDENCY! I NEED HOLISTIC HEALING AND WELLNESS BEFORE I'LL ACCEPT ANY RESPONSIBILITY FOR MY ACTIONS!

ONE OF US NEEDS TO STICK HIS HEAD IN A BUCKET OF ICE WATER.
I LOVE THE CULTURE OF VICTIMHOOD.

WHY IS THIS SNOWMAN LOOKING AT A SNOWBALL?
HE'S CONTEMPLATING SNOWMAN EVOLUTION.

OBVIOUSLY, IF HE EVOLVED FROM A SNOWBALL, IT RAISES TOUGH THEOLOGICAL QUESTIONS FOR HIM.

LIKE THE MORALITY OF THROWING ONE'S PRECURSORS AT SOMEONE?
SURE, AND WHAT ABOUT SHOVELING ONE'S GENETIC MATERIAL OFF THE WALK?

!!
PLOP

IT'S THAT MOMENT OF DAWNING COMPREHENSION I LIVE FOR.

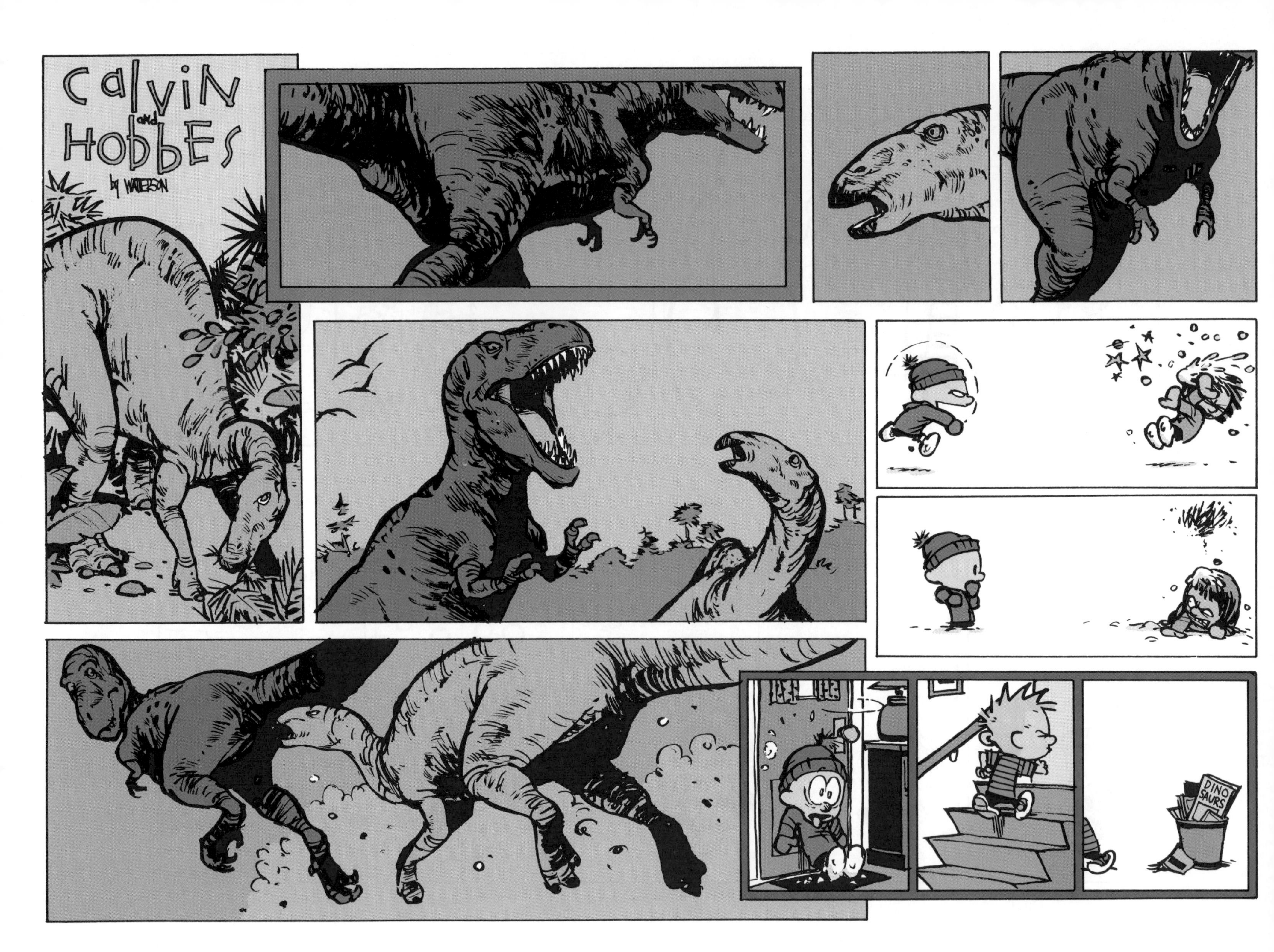
Calvin and Hobbes
by WATTERSON
DINO
SAURS

I LIKE TO VERB WORDS.
WHAT?

I TAKE NOUNS AND ADJECTIVES AND USE THEM AS VERBS. REMEMBER WHEN "ACCESS" WAS A THING? NOW IT'S SOMETHING YOU **DO**. IT GOT VERBED.

VERBING WEIRDS LANGUAGE.
MAYBE WE CAN EVENTUALLY MAKE LANGUAGE A COMPLETE IMPEDIMENT TO UNDERSTANDING.

WOW, CHOCOLATE CHIP COOKIE BATTER! I LOVE IT BEFORE IT'S COOKED! CAN I HAVE SOME? PLEASE, PLEASE?

NO, IT'S GOT RAW EGGS IN IT AND YOU COULD GET SALMONELLA POISONING.

ONE MORE NOSTALGIC PART OF CHILDHOOD GOES **THBPPTH**.

WHERE ARE MY GLASSES? I THOUGHT THEY WERE RIGHT HERE.

HMM... I PUT THEM DOWN.... I WENT TO GET MY BOOK.... I TOLD CALVIN TO SHOVEL THE WALK...

WHERE COULD THEY BE??

THE SECRET TO MAKING GREAT HOT CHOCOLATE IS TO PUT THE TINY MARSHMALLOWS IN **FIRST**.

SO THEY MELT FASTER?
NO, SO YOU CAN FIT IN 40 OR 50 OF THEM.

THIS WAY, THE HOT CHOCOLATE JUST FILLS IN THE CRACKS.

I WONDERED WHY YOU EAT IT WITH A FORK.
ALSO, I DON'T USE MILK. I JUST HEAT THE SYRUP.

WHAT ARE YOU DOING? DON'T WEAR YOUR BOOTS THROUGH THE HOUSE!

CONSIDERING WHERE MY **SHOES** HAVE BEEN, I THOUGHT SHE'D BE HAPPY.

IF YOU DO THE JOB BADLY ENOUGH, SOMETIMES YOU DON'T GET ASKED TO DO IT AGAIN.

Calvin and Hobbes by Watterson

1. Write a paragraph explaining the significance of Magellan's expedition.

A GAS MASK, A SMOKE GRENADE, AND A HELICOPTER .... THAT'S ALL I ASK.

CALVIN, DON'T JUST THROW YOUR WET COAT ON THE FLOOR!

HANG IT UP WHERE IT BELONGS! I'M NOT LOOKING FOR EXTRA WORK AROUND HERE.

OH, LIKE ***I*** AM.

I'm gonna pound you at recess, Twinky.

OH YEAH?! WELL, YOU'LL HAVE TO **CATCH** ME FIRST!

WHEN YOUR STRATEGY IS TO RUN LIKE A SQUIRREL, IT'S HARD TO COME UP WITH A GOOD TAUNT.

TODAY FOR SHOW AND TELL, I'VE BROUGHT A TINY MARVEL OF NATURE: A SINGLE SNOWFLAKE.

I THINK WE MIGHT ALL LEARN A LESSON FROM HOW THIS UTTERLY UNIQUE AND EXQUISITE CRYSTAL...

...TURNS INTO AN ORDINARY, BORING MOLECULE OF WATER, JUST LIKE EVERY OTHER ONE, WHEN YOU BRING IT IN THE CLASSROOM.

AND NOW, WHILE THE ANALOGY SINKS IN, I'LL BE LEAVING YOU DRIPS AND GOING OUTSIDE.
CALVIN!

LOOK AT THIS SANDWICH MY MOM MADE! I'M NOT EATING THIS WRETCHED THING!

WHY, THIS SQUID ISN'T EVEN FRESH! SMELL IT! LOOK HOW RUBBERY IT IS! AND THE INKY BRINE HAS SOAKED THE BREAD! THE PICKLES ARE PULP! GROSS!

WANNA TRADE?

NOBODY WILL TRADE WITH A KID WHOSE MOM MAKES A BAD SANDWICH.

YOU KNOW WHAT ASTRONAUTS CAN DO RIGHT IN THEIR SPACESUITS?

GEEZ, HOW AM I EVER GOING TO LEARN TO BE AN ASTRONAUT?

Calvin and Hobbes
by WATTERSON
WHAT AN AWFUL JOB! THIS IS THE WORST!
WELL SOMEBODY'S GOT TO DO IT.
HEADS UP!!
BLORRP!
EEWW! WHAT'S THIS?!
UGH, WHO CAN TELL?
KEEP STIRRING!!
OH NO! IT'S BUBBLING UP!
AIEE! CHEMICAL REACTION!!
LOOK OUT!

RUN! RUN!
IT'S GONNA BLOW!

FOOM!

BU-URRRPP!

CALVIN, THAT'S ENOUGH!
I CAN'T HELP IT! MY STOMACH MICROBES CAN'T HANDLE THIS AWFUL FOOD!

OH LOVELY SNOWBALL, PACKED WITH CARE, SMACK A HEAD THAT'S UNAWARE!

THEN WITH FREEZING ICE TO SPARE, MELT AND SOAK THROUGH UNDERWEAR!

FLY STRAIGHT AND TRUE, HIT HARD AND SQUARE! THIS, OH SNOWBALL, IS MY PRAYER.

I ONLY THROW CONSECRATED SNOWBALLS.

WHAT ARE YOU DOING?

I'M THROWING PEOPLE OFF MY TRAIL WITH DECEPTIVE FOOTPRINTS.

SEE EVERYONE WILL THINK THESE TRACKS WERE MADE BY A ONE-LEGGED KID GOING **THAT** WAY, AND THEY'LL BE COMPLETELY WRONG!

WHO EXACTLY IS ON YOUR TRAIL?
LOOK, IT DOESN'T HURT TO TAKE PRECAUTIONS.

NOBODY CAN MAKE ME GO INSIDE! I'VE GOT 200 SNOWBALLS THAT SAY I'M STAYING **OUT**! NO ONE'S GONNA MAKE **ME** COME IN THE HOUSE!

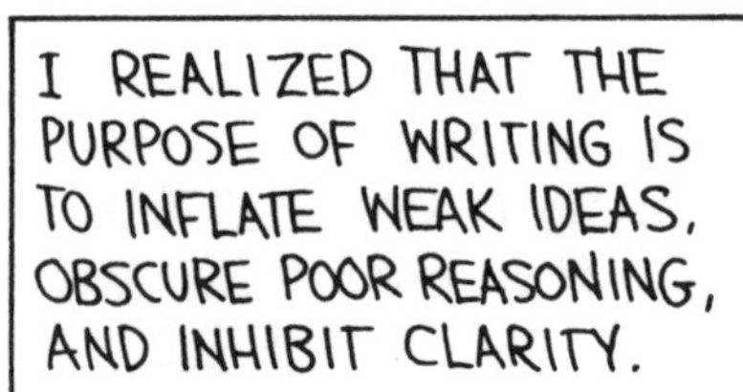

HERE WE ARE, HIGH ON RIGOR MORTIS RIDGE, STEELING OURSELVES FOR THE TERRIFYING DESCENT INTO GRIM REAPER GORGE!

WHY DO WE RISK LIFE AND LIMB IN A VERTICAL FREE FALL, WHEN WE COULD BE SAFE AT HOME BY THE FIRE?

BECAUSE IT IS MAN'S INDOMITABLE NATURE TO SCARE HIMSELF SILLY FOR NO GOOD REASON!

IF YOU MAKE IT HOME TO THE FIRE, YOU CAN TELL ME HOW IT WAS.
SEE? THIS IS WHY THERE WERE NEVER ANY GREAT ANIMAL EXPLORERS!

SMACK!

AH HA HA HA! THAT WAS HILARIOUS! HA HA HA!

POW!

A JOKE IS NEVER AS FUNNY THE SECOND TIME YOU HEAR IT.

Calvin and Hobbes
by WATTERSON
TODAY IS VALENTINE'S DAY.
SO WHAT?! WHO CARES?! NOT ME!

WHO'S YOUR VALENTINE THIS YEAR??
NOBODY!

IS IT SUSIE??
NO!

I'LL BET SHE IS! I'LL BET YOUR HEART BEATS FASTER AT THE SOUND OF HER NAME! AHH, HOW YOU LONG TO GAZE DEEP INTO HER SHIMMERING EYES!!
WHAT?!!

YOUR CHEEKS ARE FLUSHED! YOUR CHIN QUIVERS TO IMAGINE HER SOFT, WARM LIPS PRESSED AGAINST YOURS! OH, TO BE LOCKED FOR ETERNITY IN A PASSIONATE EMBRACE WITH SWEET, SWEET SUSIE!

TAKE IT BACK!
HAVE YOU PICKED OUT A RING YET?
TAKE IT BACK!
TAKE IT BACK!
CAN I BE "BEST TIGER"?
WHERE'S THE HONEY-MOON?

HEY, CALVIN!
HUH??

YOU JERK! THIS IS FOR SENDING ME A VALENTINE CARD WITH A DRAWING OF ME AS A WORM-EATEN CORPSE!

OH HO-O-O! YOU SENT HER A CARD?? DOCTOR LOVE, PAGING DOCTOR I.M.N. LOVE!
I'D SAY WE'RE ABOUT DUE FOR ANOTHER SAINT VALENTINE'S DAY MASSACRE.

IT MUST BE A ***FALLEN*** ANGEL! GENERALLY THEY BURN UP IN THE ATMOSPHERE, BUT THIS ONE APPARENTLY VAPORIZED ON IMPACT, LEAVING THIS ANGEL-SHAPED CRATER IN THE SNOW!

I'M MAKING A MONUMENTAL, HEROIC SNOW SCULPTURE.

IT WILL BE CALLED "THE TRIUMPH OF PERSEVERANCE."

VERY INSPIRING. WHAT WILL IT LOOK LIKE?
THIS.

YOU'RE THROUGH?
I'M BORED.

IMPORTANT MESSAGE → THIS WAY

IMPORTANT MESSAGE NEXT SIGN →

!
IMPORTANT MESSAGE: LOOK OUT!

IT'S LIKE SHOOTING FISH IN A BARREL.

LOOK AT THIS! THIS IS THE BIGGEST SNOWBALL IN THE WORLD!

HA HA! I CAN'T WAIT TO PLASTER SOMEBODY WITH IT!
HOW ARE YOU GOING TO PICK IT UP?

REALITY CONTINUES TO RUIN MY LIFE.
MAYBE YOU COULD PUT IT SOMEPLACE WHERE SOMEONE WILL WALK INTO IT.

I'M NOT GOING TO DO THIS HOMEWORK! C'MON, LET'S GO OUTSIDE!

NOBODY GIVES THE EVIL EYE LIKE YOUR DAD.
DID YOU SEE HOW HIS VEINS THROBBED?

Calvin and HOBBES
by WATTERSON
..SIGHHHH..

WHAT'S IN THE BIG BAG?
NOTHING **YOU** NEED TO KNOW ABOUT.

C'MON, TELL ME!
WELL, LET'S JUST SAY IT'S SOMETHING THAT MIGHT COME IN HANDY TODAY.

WHY? WHAT HAPPENS TODAY?
WE'VE GOT A HISTORY TEST, REMEMBER?

SO WHAT DID YOU BRING? A BOMB?
WOULDN'T YOU AND THE PRINCIPAL **BOTH** LIKE TO KNOW!

WHY WON'T YOU TELL ME WHAT'S IN THAT BAG?
IT'S A SEVERED HEAD.

IT IS NOT! DON'T BE DISGUSTING!
FINE. DON'T BELIEVE ME.

YOU SAID IT WOULD COME IN HANDY DURING TODAY'S TEST.
THE HEAD IS AN ORACLE. I'LL PUT IT ON MY DESK AND IT WILL TELL ME ANSWERS.

FORGET I ASKED! I DON'T EVEN CARE!
SOOOOSIE IS A BOOGER BRAAINN!
IT SPEAKS THE TRUTH!

HERE ARE YOUR TESTS. YOU MAY BEGIN.

CAN I GO GET SOMETHING FROM MY LOCKER?
WHAT DO YOU NEED?

I CAN'T TELL YOU.
THEN SIT AND DO YOUR TEST.

YOU'RE SPOILING A GREAT SURPRISE FOR THE CLASS!
IT WOULD BE A GREAT SURPRISE FOR ME IF YOU'D JUST GET TO WORK.

Test
1. When di
discove
COUGH COUGH COUGH

CAN I GET A DRINK OF WATER?
OK, BUT HURRY UP.

THIS IS A JOB FOR...

TO AVOID DETECTION WHILE CHANGING IDENTITIES, MILD-MANNERED CALVIN LEAPS INTO HIS LOCKER!

THERE HE MAKES THE STUPENDOUS TRANSFORMATION INTO....

STUPENDOUS MANNN!
DA TA DA TUM TUM
DA TA DA TUM TUM

GOSH, IT'S DARK IN HERE. WHERE'S THAT DARN HANDLE?

BANG BANG BANG
I CAN'T GET OUT!

HMM... THIS IS A REAL JOB FOR STUPENDOUS MAN!

BANG BANG BANG BANG BANG

HECK, THIS MAY EVEN BE A JOB FOR THE CUSTODIAN.

WHERE'S CALVIN? DIDN'T HE COME BACK FROM THE DRINKING FOUNTAIN?

I'LL BET HE'S AT HIS LOCKER, MISS WORMWOOD. HE BROUGHT SOMETHING SECRET IN A PAPER BAG TODAY THAT HE SAID WOULD HELP HIM ON THE TEST.

FIVE YEARS UNTIL RETIREMENT
FIVE YEARS UNTIL RETIREMENT
STUPENDOUS MAN'S STUPENDOUS POWERS ARE OF NO AVAIL IN THIS CUNNING TRAP! ZOUNDS! IT'S STUPENDOUS MAN'S FIENDISH NEMESIS, THE CRAB TEACHER, COMING TO FINISH HIM OFF!
CALVIN?

LET'S SEE IF CALVIN GOT WHATEVER WAS IN HIS LOCKER.
KA-CHUNK

WITH STUPENDOUS MUSCLES OF MAGNITUDE, STUPENDOUS MAN BREAKS FREE!!
WHAT ON EARTH?!

S... FOR STUPENDOUS!
T... FOR TIGER, FEROCITY OF!
U... FOR UNDERWEAR, RED!
P... FOR POWER, INCREDIBLE!
E... FOR EXCELLENT PHYSIQUE!
N... FOR... UM... SOMETHING... HM, WELL, I'LL COME BACK TO THAT...
D... FOR DETERMINATION!
U... FOR... WAIT, HOW DO YOU SPELL THIS? IS IT "I"??
IT'S NOT ENOUGH THAT WE HAVE TO BE DISCIPLINARIANS. NOW WE NEED TO BE PSYCHOLOGISTS.
YOUR NEFARIOUS SCHEME WILL NEVER SUCCEED!

STUPENDOUS MAN ESCAPES! A CRIMSON BOLT BURSTS THROUGH THE AIR!
CALVIN, COME BACK HERE!

NOW IT'S OFF TO APPLY MY STUPENDOUS POWERS OF CONCENTRATION TO THE HISTORY TEST OF MY ALTER EGO, MILD-MANNERED CALVIN!

TA-DAAA! HAVE NO FEAR, BOYS AND GIRLS! I'M STUPENDOUS MAN, CHAMPION OF LIBERTY AND JUSTICE!

TRY TO RESTRAIN YOURSELVES, GIRLS! I'M JUST HERE TO DO CALVIN'S TEST.
HE LIVES ON YOUR STREET, DOESN'T HE?
I HARDLY EVEN KNOW HIM, CANDACE!

STUPENDOUS MAN'S STUPENDOUS KNOWLEDGE LETS HIM COMPLETE THE TEST WITH STUPENDOUS SPEED! 1492! THE BATTLE OF LEXINGTON! TROTSKY! THE COTTON GIN!

ANOTHER TRIUMPH FOR VIRTUE AND RIGHT! AND NOW, WITH A WHOOSH, STUPENDOUS MAN IS OFF INTO THE SKY! SO LONG, KIDS! ALWAYS BRUSH YOUR TEETH! KAPWINGGG!

CLASS, DID CALVIN COME IN HERE?! HAS ANYONE SEEN HIM?
HERE I AM, MISS WORMWOOD! BOY, WAS I THIRSTY!

AAAUGHH! LET GO! LET GO! YOU'VE GOT THE WRONG GUY! I'M CALVIN! I DIDN'T DO ANYTHING WRONG!
BONK
CRASH

I JUST GOT A DRINK OF WATER! YOU SAID I COULD! STUPENDOUS MAN IS THE ONE YOU WANT! I'M NOT HIM! HELP! HELP!
SCRAPE
DRAG

CLASS, YOU SAW STUPENDOUS MAN! TELL MISS WORMWOOD! ARRGGH! HELP! I'VE BEEN FALSELY ACCUSED!
CRUNCH
CLUNK

WHEN MOM ASKS ME HOW MY DAY AT SCHOOL WAS, I ALWAYS JUST SAY, "FINE," AND CHANGE THE SUBJECT.
NO! NO!

SO THE TEACHER TOLD MOM, AND MOM HIT THE ROOF AND TOOK AWAY MY COSTUME.
YIKES.

..UM... HAS STUPENDOUS MAN EVER WON A BATTLE?
WELL, THEY'RE ALL MORAL VICTORIES.

ONE CAN'T BE PICKY.
OH, AND I FLUNKED THE TEST, TOO.

KAZAM!

KAZAM!
QUIET.

KAZAM!
WHAT DID I JUST TELL YOU?!
CALVIN, IF YOU'RE BORED, I'LL FIND SOMETHING FOR YOU TO DO!

calvin and HobbEs by WATTERSON
KAZAM!

Calvin and Hobbes

REPENT SINNERS
THE END IS NEAR
SPRING IS COMING
THEY'RE SNOWMEN PROPHETS OF DOOM.
YOU CERTAINLY TAKE THE PLEASURE OUT OF WAITING FOR DAFFODILS.

ATCHOOo!

UH OH.

I'M LEAKING BRAIN LUBRICANT.

LOOK, HOBBES. THERE'S A QUIZ IN MY NEW ISSUE OF *CHEWING* MAGAZINE. "DOES YOUR GUM DELIVER? 10 QUESTIONS SHOW WHAT YOU COULD BE MISSING!"

LET'S SEE HOW MY GUM DOES. "1. HOW HARD IS YOUR GUM AT THE BEGINNING?
A) ROCK-LIKE OR BRITTLE
B) PLEASANTLY FIRM
C) SQUISHY OR BENDY"

HMM... MY GUM IS PRETTY HARD AT FIRST. I'LL MARK "A".

GOSH, I'VE GOT NEGATIVE FIVE POINTS ALREADY! I'M NOT GETTING ALL THE PERFORMANCE I'M ENTITLED TO!
I WONDER WHAT PEOPLE KNEW BEFORE THERE WERE MAGAZINE QUIZZES.

OK, YOU'VE ALL READ THE CHAPTER, SO LET'S REVIEW.

CALVIN, WHERE WAS THE BYZANTINE EMPIRE?

I'LL TAKE "OUTER PLANETS" FOR $100.

MOM! WAKE UP! COME QUICK!
WHAT'S WRONG? WHAT'S THE MATTER?

DO YOU THINK LOVE IS NOTHING BUT A BIOCHEMICAL REACTION DESIGNED TO MAKE SURE OUR GENES GET PASSED ON?

WHATEVER IT IS, IT'S ALL THAT'S KEEPING ME FROM STRANGLING YOU RIGHT NOW.

MOM'S MIDNIGHT REASSURANCES ARE NEVER VERY REASSURING.
WATTERSON

WHEN YOU'RE A KID, YOU DON'T HAVE MUCH VARIETY OF EXPERIENCE.

YOU LIVE WITH YOUR PARENTS AND THAT'S ALL YOU KNOW. YOU GROW UP THINKING WHATEVER THEY DO IS "NORMAL."

AHH, WHAT A DAY! UP AT 6:00, A 10-MILE RUN IN THE SLEET, AND **NOW** A BIG BOWL OF PLAIN OATMEAL! HOW I LOVE THE CRAZY HEDONISM OF WEEKENDS!

WELL, MAYBE "NORMAL" IS TOO STRONG A WORD.
I THINK WE'D KNOW NORMAL IF WE SAW IT.
WATTERSON

Calvin and HOBBES
by WATTERSON
MOOOO MOOO MOOOO
WHOOSH KACHUNK CHUG CHUG
SQUEAK SQUEAK SQUEAK
CLANG CLANG
WIZZ WIRP BOINGG WIZZ WIRP BOINGG
AWKK! HELLO! HELLO!
GAAAA GGHHH
RIP
BONK BONK
GASP GASP

BOY, AM I GLAD TO SEE *YOU*, HOBBES!

ANOTHER TYPICAL SCHOOL DAY?

RRGGGH.... 125 ....

OOF

RRRGGH... 5,200!

EXERCISE IS A LOT MORE GRATIFYING IF YOU COUNT WHAT IT *FEELS* LIKE.

I DON'T WANT TO GET UP. I DON'T WANT TO GET DRESSED. I DON'T WANT TO WAIT FOR THE BUS.

I DON'T WANT TO GO TO SCHOOL. I DON'T WANT TO LISTEN TO THE TEACHER.

I DON'T WANT TO STUDY. I DON'T WANT ANY TESTS. I DON'T WANT ANY HOMEWORK.

HOW WAS YOUR DAY?
IT PITCHED A PERFECT NO-HITTER.

YOU KNOW, THERE MUST BE THOUSANDS OF ANIMAL SPECIES, AND OF **ALL** OF THEM, ONLY HUMANS WEAR CLOTHES.

ISN'T THAT WEIRD? I WONDER WHY OTHER ANIMALS DON'T WEAR CLOTHES.

IF OUR NAKED PINK BUTTS SHOWED, WE PROBABLY WOULD.
OUR BUTTS ARE JUST FINE!
WATTERSON

I'M GOING OUTSIDE.
ARE YOU DONE WITH YOUR HOMEWORK?

YES.
YOU READ THAT WHOLE CHAPTER?

LET'S JUST LEAVE IT THAT I'M DONE.
BACK TO YOUR ROOM, BUSTER.
WATTERSON

I'LL BET SOME KIDS WALK AROUND CORNERS WITHOUT EVEN THINKING ABOUT IT.
THAT WAS A ROTTEN TRICK.

GRAVITY MUST PULL ESPECIALLY HARD ON TIGERS.
THAT'S AN IMPRESSION WE LIKE TO CULTIVATE.

FOR EXAMPLE, SCIENTISTS THINK SPACE IS FULL OF MYSTERIOUS, INVISIBLE MASS, SO WHAT DO THEY CALL IT? "**DARK** MATTER"! **DUHH**! I TELL YOU, THERE'S A FORTUNE TO BE MADE HERE!

MISS WORMWOOD, I PROTEST THIS "C" GRADE! THAT'S SAYING I ONLY DID AN "AVERAGE" JOB!

I GOT 75% OF THE ANSWERS CORRECT, AND IN TODAY'S SOCIETY, DOING SOMETHING 75% RIGHT IS OUTSTANDING! IF GOVERNMENT AND INDUSTRY WERE 75% COMPETENT, WE'D BE ECSTATIC!

I WON'T STAND FOR THIS ARTIFICIAL STANDARD OF PERFORMANCE! I DEMAND AN "A" FOR THIS KIND OF WORK!

I THINK IT'S REALLY GROSS HOW SHE DRINKS MAALOX STRAIGHT FROM THE BOTTLE.

HISTORY WILL THANK ME FOR KEEPING THIS JOURNAL AT SUCH A YOUNG AGE.

AS ONE OF THOSE RARE INDIVIDUALS DESTINED FOR TRUE GREATNESS, THIS RECORD OF MY THOUGHTS AND CONVICTIONS WILL PROVIDE INVALUABLE INSIGHT INTO BUDDING GENIUS.

THINK OF IT! A PRICELESS HISTORICAL DOCUMENT IN THE MAKING! WOW!

..SO WHO **ELSE** SHOULD I ADD TO MY LIST OF TOTAL JERKS?
WHO ELSE DO YOU EVEN KNOW?
WATTERSON

WAIT, DAD! I'VE GOT A GREAT IDEA!

DON'T SHAVE NEXT TO YOUR MOUTH, OK? LET THE WHISKERS GROW ABOUT A FOOT LONG AND THEN WAX 'EM SO THEY STICK STRAIGHT OUT! THEN YOU'LL LOOK LIKE A BIG CAT!

DAD DIDN'T THINK THE FIRM WOULD GO FOR IT.
PREPOSTEROUS!

"TIGER! TIGER! BURNING BRIGHT, IN THE FORESTS OF THE NIGHT."

BLAKE WROTE THAT. APPARENTLY THE TIGER WAS ON FIRE. MAYBE HIS TAIL GOT STRUCK BY LIGHTNING OR SOMETHING.

FLAMMABLE FELINES - WHAT A WEIRD SUBJECT FOR POETRY.

THIS IS WHY I TRY TO SLEEP THROUGH MOST OF THE DAY.

Calvin and Hobbes by Watterson

BORRRING

YEAH, YEAH... KILL THE MESSENGER.
PRINCIPAL

HELLO, COUNTY LIBRARY? REFERENCE DESK, PLEASE. THANK YOU.

HELLO? YES, I NEED A BOOK ON PAINTING THEORY AND TECHNIQUE.

SPECIFICALLY, I'M INTERESTED IN GRAFFITI. IS THERE A BOOK THAT EXPLAINS THE PROPER USE OF MATERIALS AND LISTS POPULAR DIRTY WORDS AND SLOGANS?

WHAT ON EARTH DO THEY SPEND THEIR MONEY ON OVER THERE?

Calvin:
MEMOIRS of a
SIX-YEAR-OLD

My LIFE HAS BEEN a fascinating SERIES of amazing EXPLOITS, about WHICH I HAVE MANY profound INSIGHTS.

But FRANKLY, NONE of it is ANY of YOUR darn BUSINESS, so butt out!
THE END.

DO PUBLISHERS DEMAND THAT MANUSCRIPTS BE TYPED?
I WOULDN'T SWEAT IT.
WATTERSON

AAUGH! THE PEANUT BUTTER IS RUINED!

YOU'RE SUPPOSED TO SCOOP ONE HALF STRAIGHT DOWN AND THEN DIG OUT THE OTHER SIDE FROM THE BOTTOM, SO PART OF THE TOP REMAINS UNDISTURBED UNTIL THE VERY END!

WHAT ON EARTH FOR?
IT'S A RITUAL! YOU HAVE TO KEEP THE TOP OF THE PEANUT BUTTER SMOOTH!

MAYBE YOU SHOULD MAKE YOUR OWN SANDWICHES.
IF YOU CAN'T CONTROL YOUR PEANUT BUTTER, YOU CAN'T EXPECT TO CONTROL YOUR LIFE. DID YOU CUT THE BREAD DIAGONALLY?

AAAUGH! AAUGHH!
SOMETHING'S CRAWLING DOWN MY LEG! GET IT OUT!

...OH, IT'S JUST A COUPLE OF PENNIES. I'VE GOT A HOLE IN MY POCKET.
* WHEW *

YOU NEVER KNOW WHEN SOME CRAZED RODENT WITH COLD FEET MIGHT BE RUNNING LOOSE IN YOUR PANTS.
ANOTHER REASON NOT TO WEAR 'EM.

DO YOU THINK BABIES ARE BORN SINFUL? THAT THEY COME INTO THE WORLD AS SINNERS?

NO, I THINK THEY'RE JUST QUICK STUDIES.

WHENEVER YOU DISCUSS CERTAIN THINGS WITH ANIMALS, YOU GET INSULTED.

Calvin and Hobbes
by WATTERSON
15 BUCKS A GLASS ?!
THAT'S RIGHT! WANT SOME ?
LEMONadE $15.00 GLASS
HOW DO YOU JUSTIFY CHARGING 15 DOLLARS ?!
SUPPLY AND DEMAND.

WHERE'S THE DEMAND ?! I DON'T SEE ANY DEMAND!
THERE'S **LOTS** OF DEMAND!
LEMONadE $15.00 GLASS

YEAH ?
SURE! AS THE SOLE STOCKHOLDER IN THIS ENTERPRISE, I **DEMAND** MONSTROUS PROFIT ON MY INVESTMENT!

AND AS PRESIDENT AND C.E.O. OF THE COMPANY, I **DEMAND** AN EXORBITANT ANNUAL SALARY!

AND AS MY OWN EMPLOYEE, I **DEMAND** A HIGH HOURLY WAGE AND ALL SORTS OF COMPANY BENEFITS! AND **THEN** THERE'S OVERHEAD AND ACTUAL PRODUCTION COSTS!
LEMONadE $15.00 GLASS

BUT IT LOOKS LIKE YOU JUST THREW A LEMON IN SOME SLUDGE WATER!
WELL, I HAVE TO CUT EXPENSES **SOME**WHERE IF I WANT TO STAY COMPETITIVE.

WHAT IF I GOT SICK FROM THAT?
"CAVEAT EMPTOR" IS THE MOTTO WE STAND BEHIND! I'D HAVE TO CHARGE MORE IF WE FOLLOWED HEALTH AND ENVIRONMENTAL REGULATIONS.

YOU'RE OUT OF YOUR MIND. I'M GOING HOME TO DRINK SOMETHING ELSE.
SURE! PUT ME OUT OF A JOB! IT'S YOU ANTI-BUSINESS TYPES WHO RUIN THE ECONOMY!
LEMONadE $15.00 GLASS

LEMONadE $15.00 GLASS

I NEED TO BE SUBSIDIZED.

THE TV LISTINGS SAY THIS MOVIE HAS "ADULT SITUATIONS." WHAT ARE ADULT SITUATIONS?

PROBABLY THINGS LIKE GOING TO WORK, PAYING BILLS AND TAXES, TAKING RESPONSIBILITIES...

WOW, THEY DON'T KID AROUND WHEN THEY SAY "FOR MATURE AUDIENCES."
I'VE NEVER UNDERSTOOD HOW THOSE MOVIES MAKE ANY MONEY.

BANG
CLANG
WHANG

ZANG
PANG
BLANG

WILL YOU STOP THAT AWFUL RACKET?! YOU'RE DRIVING ME CRAZY!

..AND A CHECK MARK FOR TUESDAY!

MISS WORMWOOD?
YES, CALVIN?

MY GENERATION DOESN'T ABSORB INFORMATION THIS WAY. COULD YOU REDUCE EVERYTHING TO FACTOIDS?
TURN TO PAGE 21, CLASS.

AT LEAST OUR TELEVISIONS UNDERSTAND US.

I HATE IT WHEN IT'S THIS WINDY.
YOU KNOW WHAT *I* HATE? I HATE WHEN I'M TALKING AND SOMEONE TURNS THE CONVERSATION TO HIMSELF!

IT'S SO RUDE! WHY DO THEY THINK I'M TALKING?! IT'S SO THEY CAN HEAR ABOUT *ME*! WHO CARES WHAT *THEY* HAVE TO SAY! IF I START A CONVERSATION, IT SHOULD STAY ON THE SUBJECT OF *ME*!

I ALSO HATE IT WHEN PEOPLE LOOK AT ME ALL BUG-EYED.
THAT MUST HAPPEN A LOT.

HOW MaNY BOaRdS Would tHE MONGOLS HOaRd, if tHE MONGOL HORdES Got BORED?

NO SENSE PUTTING IT OFF. IT'S TIME FOR SPRING CLEANING.
GOOD FOR YOU.

WHAT ABOUT THE **HOUSE**?
WHAT **ABOUT** THE HOUSE?

calvin and HOBBES by WATTERSON

AT LAST, SOME CLARITY! EVERY SENTENCE IS EITHER PURE, SWEET TRUTH OR A VILE, CONTEMPTIBLE LIE! ONE OR THE OTHER! NOTHING IN BETWEEN!

I'M AT PEACE WITH THE WORLD. I'M COMPLETELY SERENE.
WHY IS THAT?

I'VE DISCOVERED MY PURPOSE IN LIFE. I KNOW WHY I WAS PUT HERE AND WHY EVERYTHING EXISTS.

OH REALLY?
YES, I AM HERE SO EVERYBODY CAN DO WHAT I WANT.

IT'S NICE TO HAVE THAT CLEARED UP.
ONCE EVERYONE ACCEPTS IT, THEY'LL BE SERENE TOO.

AHH, SPRING!

I SAY LET'S MOVE ON TO SUMMER.

I THRIVE ON CHANGE.
YOU?!

YOU THREW A FIT THIS MORNING BECAUSE YOUR MOM PUT LESS JELLY ON YOUR TOAST THAN YESTERDAY!

I THRIVE ON MAKING **OTHER** PEOPLE CHANGE.

EWW, MUD.

LOOK AT THIS GOOSHY, DIRTY, SLIMY, THICK WET MUCK!

BLECCHH.

TALK ABOUT A KID MAGNET!

Calvin and HOBBES
by WATTERSON
IT ALL BOILS DOWN TO LUCK, HOBBES. SOME PEOPLE ARE BORN LUCKY AND SOME PEOPLE ARE BORN **UN**LUCKY.
EITHER WAY, THERE'S NOTHING YOU CAN DO ABOUT IT. YOU CAN'T FIGHT LUCK.
WE'RE HEADED FOR THAT CLIFF!
YIKES! BAD LUCK!
'BYE.
SEE WHAT I MEAN?! YOU GO ALONG, MINDING YOUR OWN BUSINESS, AND SUDDENLY YOUR LUCK RUNS OUT!
IF YOU'RE-**OW**-UNLUCKY, WHAT CAN YOU DO? **OW!** YOU'RE CONDEMNED TO SUFFER! **OW!**
OOH, RIGHT IN THE PRICKER BUSHES. ...JUST LIKE YESTERDAY.
MAYBE MY LUCK WILL CHANGE TOMORROW.

SUSIE, I THINK IT'S ONLY FAIR TO TELL YOU THAT THERE IS ABSOLUTELY NO WAY I WOULD EVEN **CONSIDER** ASKING YOU TO THE SENIOR PROM.

THAT'S ELEVEN **YEARS** FROM NOW!
I FIGURE THAT MIGHT GIVE YOU ENOUGH TIME TO FIND SOMEBODY WHO WILL.

IF I'D KNOWN HER LONGER, I COULD'VE GIVEN HER MORE NOTICE.

Z

I THINK TIGERS ARE ACTUALLY CLASSIFIED AS LIQUIDS.
HAR HAR.

"F"?!

IT SEEMS TO ME THAT IF I'M NOT LEARNING THIS MATERIAL, YOU MUST NOT BE A VERY GOOD TEACHER!

WOGGA MUK GUBBA PUM WUP! BOO! GOP!

WHAT??
WATTERSON

IS THIS MILK SPOILED?
SMELL IT AND SEE.

I'M NOT GOING TO SMELL IT! YOU SMELL IT!

OH, FOR GOODNESS' SAKE, HERE. ..IT'S FINE.
MILK

I DON'T TAKE CHANCES WITH A PRODUCT THAT PRINTS THE DATE YOU MIGHT EXPIRE.
WATTERSON

CURIOSITY IS THE ESSENCE OF THE SCIENTIFIC MIND.

FOR EXAMPLE, YOU KNOW HOW MILK COMES OUT YOUR NOSE IF YOU LAUGH WHILE DRINKING?

WELL, I'M GOING TO SEE WHAT HAPPENS WHEN I INHALE MILK *INTO* MY NOSE AND LAUGH!

IDIOCY IS THE ESSENCE OF THE MALE MIND.
I'M GUESSING IT WILL SHOOT OUT MY EARS. DON'T YOU WANT TO SEE?!
WATTERSON

I THINK I'LL COUNT ALL THE ROCKS I CAN FIND.

400 TRILLION AND THREE, 400 TRILLION AND FOUR, 400 TRILLION AND FIVE...

WOW, I BORED MYSELF *AWAKE*.
WATERSON

Calvin and Hobbes by Watterson

Calvin and Hobbes
by WATTERSON

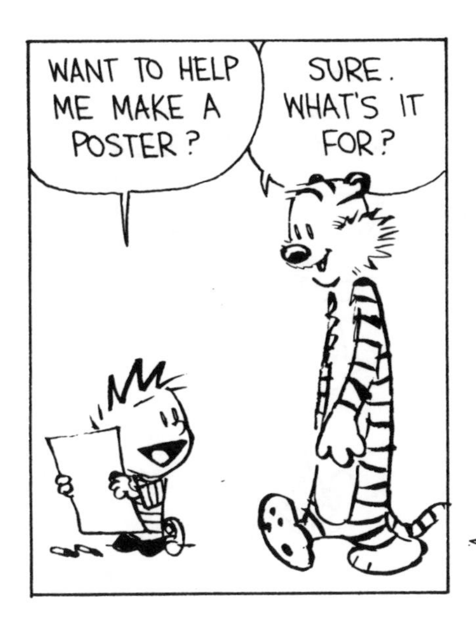
WANT TO HELP ME MAKE A POSTER?
SURE. WHAT'S IT FOR?

IT'S A SCHOOL CONTEST. WE'RE SUPPOSED TO DO TRAFFIC SAFETY POSTERS. THE WINNER GETS FIVE BUCKS!

WOW!
THINK OF IT! WE'LL BE RICH! AND THEN THERE'S THE FAME AND GLORY! I TELL YOU, THIS COULD BE OUR TICKET OUT OF THIS TWO-BIT DUMP!

SOUNDS GOOD. WHAT'S OUR WINNING POSTER GOING TO SAY?
THAT'S WHERE **YOU** COME IN.

OUR TRAFFIC SAFETY POSTER NEEDS A CATCHY SLOGAN THAT PROMOTES AWARENESS AND CAUTION. ANY IDEAS?

HOW ABOUT, "DON'T LOOK INTO CAR HEADLIGHTS AND FREEZE, BECAUSE YOU'LL EITHER GET RUN OVER OR SHOT!"

I'LL CHECK THE STATISTICS, BUT I DON'T THINK THAT HAPPENS TO MANY PEOPLE.
THERE'S MORE TO THIS WORLD THAN JUST PEOPLE, YOU KNOW.

HEY DAD, I'M DOING A TRAFFIC SAFETY POSTER. DO YOU HAVE ANY IDEAS FOR A SLOGAN?

SURE! "CYCLISTS HAVE A RIGHT TO THE ROAD TOO, YOU NOISY, POLLUTING, INCONSIDERATE MANIACS! I HOPE GAS GOES UP TO EIGHT BUCKS A GALLON!"

THANKS, DAD. I'LL GO ASK MOM.
WHY? THAT'S A **GREAT** SLOGAN!

MOM SUGGESTED THE SLOGAN, "BEFORE YOU CROSS, LOOK EACH WAY... AND YOU'LL GET HOME SAFE EACH DAY."

THAT'S KIND OF CATCHY.
YEAH, BUT I LIKE **MY** IDEA BETTER.

"BE CAREFUL, OR BE ROADKILL!"

I SUPPOSE THAT LENDS ITSELF MORE TO YOUR PARTICULAR BRAND OF ILLUSTRATION.
I HOPE I HAVE ENOUGH CADMIUM RED.

WITH MY GREAT SLOGAN AND YOUR GREAT ARTWORK, THIS TRAFFIC SAFETY POSTER IS A SHOO-IN FOR FIRST PRIZE!

A SOLID FOUNDATION OF ANATOMICAL STUDY IS ESSENTIAL FOR THE ARTIST.
WHAT SHOULD WE SPEND THE PRIZE MONEY ON?

OF COURSE, TECHNICAL SKILL ALONE ISN'T ENOUGH. A PICTURE NEEDS DEPTH OF FEELING.
I THINK I'LL BLOW IT ALL ON JAW BREAKERS AND COMIC BOOKS.

I'LL DRAW SOME STARS TO SHOW PAIN AND HUMAN SUFFERING.
WHEN YOU'VE GOT TALENT LIKE OURS, THE WORLD IS YOUR OYSTER.

THERE! FINISHED!
HEY, THAT'S TERRIFIC! WHEN WE WIN FIRST PRIZE, I'LL GIVE YOU 25% OF THE WINNINGS.

WHAT?! I DID ALL THE DRAWING! **YOU** SHOULD GET 25%!
BUT IT WAS **MY** GREAT IDEA! WE'LL SPLIT 60-40.

50-50.
OH, ALL RIGHT, **BE** SELFISH!

A GOOD COMPROMISE LEAVES EVERYBODY MAD.

HI CALVIN.
I SEE YOU WASTED YOUR TIME DRAWING A SAFETY POSTER FOR THE SCHOOL CONTEST.

I DIDN'T WASTE MY TIME!
SURE YOU DID. THE WINNING ENTRY IS RIGHT HERE. THE PRIZE IS AS GOOD AS MINE.
BE CAREFUL OR BE

"BE CAREFUL OR BE ROADKILL!" THAT'S REALLY DISGUSTING.
THANK YOU.

WHAT **IS** THAT ALL OVER THE DRAWING?
CHUNKY SPAGHETTI SAUCE!
BE CAREFUL OR

WHO WOULD LIKE TO SHOW HIS OR HER TRAFFIC SAFETY POSTER FIRST?
I WOULD! I WOULD!

ALL RIGHT, CALVIN. STEP UP FRONT.
THANK YOU! MY POSTER SAYS, "BE CAREFUL, OR BE ROADKILL!"

DRAWN IN PATENT-PENDING "3-D GORE-O-RAMA," THIS PICTURE WILL ACTUALLY ATTRACT FLIES, BECAUSE THE DRAWING IS SPLATTERED WITH SPAGHETTI SAUCE!
BE CAREFUL

I CAN SEE YOU'RE ALL JUST SICK ABOUT YOUR CHANCES OF WINNING.

WELL HOBBES, ALL WE HAVE TO DO NOW IS WAIT FOR THE JUDGES TO AWARD OUR POSTER FIRST PRIZE, AND WE'LL BE ROLLING IN MOOLAH AND PRESTIGE.

YOU KNOW, WE REALLY OUGHT TO ENTER MORE CONTESTS. I NEVER REALIZED HOW MUCH FUN IT IS TO WIN!

BUT WE HAVEN'T WON **YET**.
BUT WE **WILL**, AND THEN EVERYONE WILL KNOW HOW GREAT WE ARE.

DON'T THEY ALREADY?
OH, YOU KNOW HOW PEOPLE ARE. THEY ONLY RECOGNIZE GREATNESS WHEN SOME AUTHORITY CONFIRMS IT.

CALVIN WINS
POSTER CONTE
Judges Astounded By Quality; Boy Rakes In Cash, Shares With Tiger
Classmates Shamed By Wunderkind's Incredible Talent

LOCAL PARADE FOR POSTER WINNER
Calvin Drives Fire Engine; Few Injured
Jubilant crowds lined the streets yesterday as Safety Poster Contest Winner Calvin drove a fire truck haphazardly through town in a victory celebration. With bells ringing and sirens screaming, the young lad careened over curbs and across lawns at speeds in excess of 50 mph. Onlookers dove for cover, and amazingly, few people were
EXCLUSIVE INTERVIEW
Boy Tells Secret Of Greatness

Town Hall Razed, Statue of Calvin Commissioned for Site
NEW STATE MOTTO: "BE CAREFUL, OR BE ROADKILL!"
rsting with pride, the
yor announced today
though of historic importance, the building was "an eyesore," according to the mayor, who pushed the button that sent Town Hall flying in a cloud of debris. The statue that replaces it will be 80 ft. high and visible from several counties. Plans to make the hand wave were discarded due to expense and

LOOK CALVIN, MY POSTER **WON**!
HUH?!

OUR POSTER DIDN'T WIN?
I STILL CAN'T BELIEVE IT.

WHAT A MISCARRIAGE OF JUSTICE! THIS CONTEST WAS A JOKE! OBVIOUSLY THE JUDGES WERE BIASED AGAINST US FROM THE START!

WELL, THE IMPORTANT THING IS THAT WE TRIED OUR BEST.
THE **IMPORTANT** THING IS THAT WE **LOST**!

OOPS, I ALWAYS FORGET THE PURPOSE OF COMPETITION IS TO DIVIDE PEOPLE INTO WINNERS AND LOSERS.
WHAT'S THE POINT OF TRYING IF YOU CAN'T BE A WINNER?

DAD, MY POSTER DIDN'T WIN THE CONTEST! I THINK THE JUDGES WERE ON THE TAKE AND THE WHOLE THING WAS RIGGED!

I WANT YOU TO CALL THE SCHOOL BOARD, HAVE THEM DECLARE FRAUD, AND MAKE THEM TAKE THE PRIZE AWAY FROM SUSIE AND GIVE IT TO **ME**!

CALVIN, LOSING IS A PART OF LIFE. YOU SHOULD LEARN TO BE A GOOD SPORT ABOUT IT AND KEEP THINGS IN PERSPECTIVE. AFTER ALL, WINNING ISN'T EVERYTHING.

IS THAT REALLY WHAT THEY BELIEVE ON THE PLANET YOU'RE FROM?
YOU'VE BEEN WATCHING ATHLETIC SHOE ADS AGAIN, HAVEN'T YOU?

Calvin and Hobbes by WATTERSON

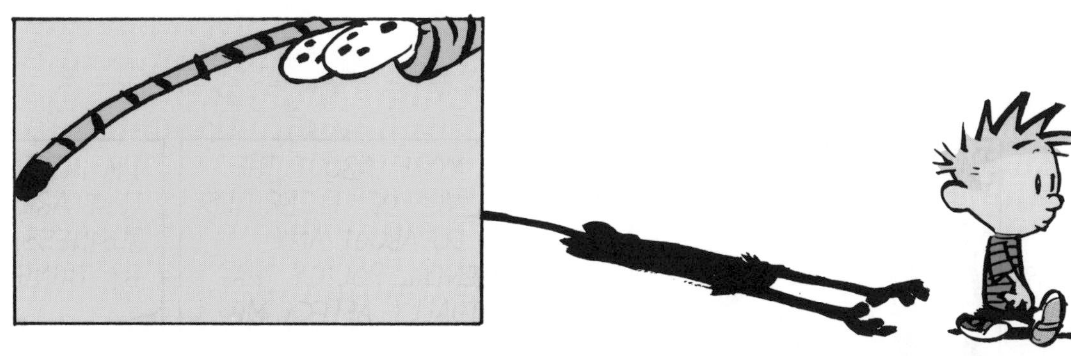

I KNOW MORE ABOUT THE PRIVATE LIVES OF CELEBRITIES THAN I DO ABOUT ANY GOVERNMENTAL POLICY THAT WILL ACTUALLY AFFECT ME.
WATTERSON

I'M INTERESTED IN THINGS THAT ARE NONE OF MY BUSINESS, AND I'M BORED BY THINGS THAT ARE IMPORTANT TO KNOW.

THE MEDIA AIM TO PLEASE.
MAYBE THE ECONOMY SHOULD BE DISCUSSED IN CHEAP MOTEL ROOMS.

A MILLION THINGS THAT BUG ME
1. DRIED-OUT CATSUP ON THE BOTTLE RIM.
2. TOAST CRUMBS IN THE BUTTER.

3. MUSHY BANANAS.
4. WORMS ON THE SIDEWALK.
5. SKIN ON PUDDING.
6. MAKING A HAND GESTURE FOR QUOTATION MARKS.
7. RAISINS.

HOW ABOUT "EXCESSIVELY NEGATIVE PEOPLE"?
YEAH, THAT'S A GOOD ONE.
...HEY!
WATTERSON

WANT TO SEE ME JUGGLE? I CAN KEEP A DOZEN EGGS IN THE AIR AT ONCE!

HUHH!

ACKPTH!
SPLOTCH
CRITCH
SPLAT
CRUNCH
CRAK

NOTICE I DIDN'T SAY I COULD DO IT VERY LONG.
THIS RUG MUST NEED A THICKER PAD.

THIS TIGER IS SPRAWLED SO STILL AND SO FLAT, A QUESTION ARISES WHEN GLANCING THEREAT.

IS HE ASLEEP? TO BE PERFECTLY FRANK, HE LOOKS MORE AS IF HE WAS CREAMED BY A TANK!

AAAUGH

DO YOU BELIEVE IN EVOLUTION?
NO.

YOU DON'T THINK HUMANS EVOLVED FROM MONKEYS?
I SURE DON'T SEE ANY DIFFERENCE.

WOO HOO HOO!

THERE'S NOTHING GOOD ON TV.
THEN TURN IT OFF.

TURN IT **OFF**?? YOU MEAN I SHOULD JUST SIT HERE STARING AT A BLANK SCREEN ALL DAY?!

OH.

KACHUNGGG

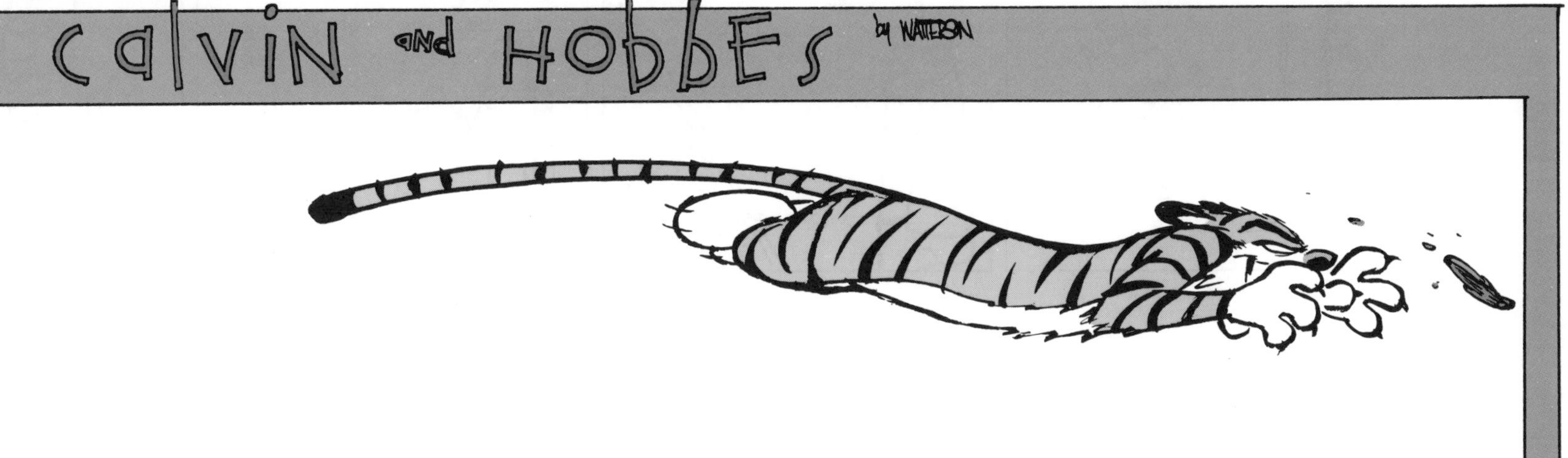
Calvin and HOBBES
by WATTERSON

THAT CERTAINLY WAS A GRIM SPECTACLE.
I *LIKE* BREAKFAST ON THE RUN.
CRUNCH CRUNCH

WHY CAN'T YOU EAT AT THE TABLE LIKE A CIVILIZED HUMAN BEING?!
BUT MOM, IT'S THEIR *NATURE*!

LET'S FIND SOME SLUGS AND WORMS.

WHY DO WE WANT TO FIND SLUGS AND WORMS?
BECAUSE THEY'RE GROSS.

THAT'S WHY ONE **AVOIDS** SLUGS AND WORMS.
IF WE AVOID THEM, WE CAN'T DARE EACH OTHER TO EAT ONE.

TOODLE-OO.
WHAT'S THE MATTER WITH YOU?! DON'T YOU LIKE **FUN**?!
WATTERSON

HEY SUSIE! DO YOU DARE ME TO EAT THIS WORM??

JUST ONE?
UM... WELL, YEAH. DON'T YOU THINK THAT'S DISGUSTING? SEE HIM WRIGGLE?

EATING FIVE AT ONCE WOULD BE DISGUSTING. I DON'T KNOW ABOUT JUST ONE.
YOU WANT ME TO EAT **FIVE**?! GEEEEZ!

WHO'D HAVE THOUGHT DISGUST WOULD BE SO INFLATIONARY?!
WATTERSON

OK SUSIE, I GOT FIVE WORMS, BUT IT WILL COST YOU 50 CENTS TO SEE ME EAT THEM.

50 CENTS ?! I'D ONLY PAY 50 CENTS IF YOU ATE 50 WORMS.
THAT'S JUST A PENNY A WORM!

RIGHT. I'LL GIVE YOU A NICKEL TO EAT THOSE FIVE.
FIVE CENTS ?! WHAT IF I HAVE TO GO TO THE HOSPITAL BECAUSE OF THIS?

OH, ALL RIGHT. I'LL THROW IN ANOTHER NICKEL IF YOU GO TO THE HOSPITAL.
..NOT SO FAST! FIRST, PROVE YOU EVEN HAVE TWO NICKELS!
WATTERSON

OK, GIVE ME THE NICKEL AND I'LL EAT THE WORMS.
NO, YOU EAT THE WORMS AND THEN I'LL GIVE YOU THE NICKEL.

HOW ABOUT TWO CENTS UP FRONT AND THE REST UPON COMPLETING THE JOB?
SORRY! YOU DON'T GET PAID UNTIL YOU DO THE WORK.

MAN, YOU'D THINK THE GUY EATING THE WORMS WOULD BE CALLING THE SHOTS!
USUALLY, IF YOU'RE CALLING ANY SHOTS AT ALL, YOU'RE NOT EATING WORMS.
WATTERSON

READY? FIVE WORMS DOWN THE HATCH! HERE GOES!

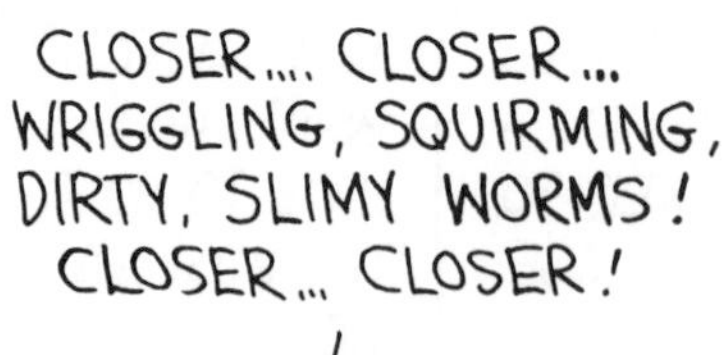
CLOSER.... CLOSER... WRIGGLING, SQUIRMING, DIRTY, SLIMY WORMS! CLOSER... CLOSER!

BOY, THEY'RE REALLY CLOSE NOW! HOW REVOLTING! CLOSER... CLOSER!

UM... FEEL FREE TO RUN AWAY SCREAMING ANY TIME.
NOT WITH MY NICKEL AT STAKE.

CALVIN, **WHAT** ARE YOU DOING?
I'M EATING WORMS FOR A NICKEL!

NO YOU'RE NOT! TIME FOR YOU TO COME HOME! AND SUSIE, IT'S MEAN TO TAKE ADVANTAGE OF KIDS WITH NO COMMON SENSE.
AW MOM, YOU SPOIL EVERYTHING!

WHAT A RELIEF! THANKS MOM. GREAT TIMING.
IF I HAVEN'T SEEN YOU FOR TWO MINUTES, I FIGURE THERE'S TROUBLE.

Calvin and Hobbes
by WATTERSON

WAP!

OH MAN, THERE GOES THE GAME!

WHAT A DUMB SPORT. I HATE BASEBALL.

WHAT'S THE USE OF TRYING?

I HAVEN'T STARTED AROUND THE BA-ASES YET!
HUH?

LA DE DA DA! I'M WALKINNNGG!

OH, LOOK AT THE PRETTY FLOWER! I THINK I'LL STOP AND SMELL IT!
OOOOOOOOOOH

UH OH! MY SHOE'S UNTIED! BETTER HAVE A SEAT AND TIE IT!

NOW I'M HOPPING BACKWARDS!
RRRRRRRR

LOOK AT ME! I'M CRAWLING! I'M A TINY LITTLE INCHWORM, MOVING AN INCH AT A TIME!

INCHY-SQUINCHY! INCHY-SQUINCHY!

AAAIEEE
WHOOP! TOO LATE! HOME RUN!

STITCHES FOR HOBBES, BANDAGES FOR YOU... HOW ON EARTH DID YOU DO THIS TO YOURSELF?
DON'T FEEL SORRY FOR HIM! HE-OW-DESERVED IT!

LITTLE JOYS OF LIFE
1. READING A NEW COMIC BOOK.
2. PETTING A HAPPY DOG.
3. GETTING A LETTER IN THE MAIL.
4. EATING THE MARSHMALLOWS IN HOT CHOCOLATE.

5. SMILING WHEN A BIG KID CALLS YOU A NASTY NAME... AND THEN PUNCHING HIS TEETH STRAIGHT DOWN HIS UGLY NECK.

YOU REALLY PULL THE OL' HEARTSTRINGS.
SOME OF THESE I HAVEN'T PERSONALLY EXPERIENCED, SAD TO SAY.
WATTERSON

LOOK HOBBES, THIS WORLD IS KIND OF LIKE TV.
WATTERSON
A CASUAL OBSERVER MIGHT EVEN CONFUSE THE TWO. BUT IF YOU NOTICE, HERE THE COLORS ARE LESS INTENSE AND THE PEOPLE ARE UGLIER.

ALSO, I SEE THAT SEVERAL MINUTES CAN GO BY WITHOUT A SINGLE CAR CHASE, EXPLOSION, MURDER OR PAT PERSONAL EXCHANGE.

WHY SETTLE FOR LESS, HMM?
SHH, THIS IS MY FAVORITE DEODORANT COMMERCIAL.

CANDID OPINIONS

YOU'RE A BAT-FACED, BUG-EYED, BOOGER-NOSED, BALONEY-BRAINED, BEETLE-BUTT!
!
CANDID OPINIONS

THIS VOLUNTEER SOCIAL WORK JUST ISN'T FOR ME.

TODAY FOR SHOW AND TELL, I'VE BROUGHT IN SOME FLASH CARDS I MADE.

EACH CARD HAS A LETTER FOLLOWED BY SEVERAL DASHES. WHEN I SHOW THE CARD, YOU YELL THE VULGAR, OBSCENE OR BLASPHEMOUS WORD THEY STAND FOR! ... READY?

SHE'S SUCH A HYPOCRITE ABOUT BUILDING VOCABULARY.

I BELIEVE PERSONAL GREED JUSTIFIES EVERYTHING.

ALSO, PRIVATE LIVES ARE LEGITIMATE PUBLIC ENTERTAINMENT.

AND THE LOWEST COMMON DENOMINATOR IS ALWAYS RIGHT!

DO I HAVE CAREER OPTIONS, OR WHAT?
I THINK I NEED TO START HANGING AROUND WITH OTHER ANIMALS.

OOH! AHH! EEE!

POP

IT COULD'VE HAPPENED!
ONLY CORN DOES THAT. ADD SOME COLD WATER AND GET BACK IN THE TUB.

Calvin and Hobbes

by WATTERSON

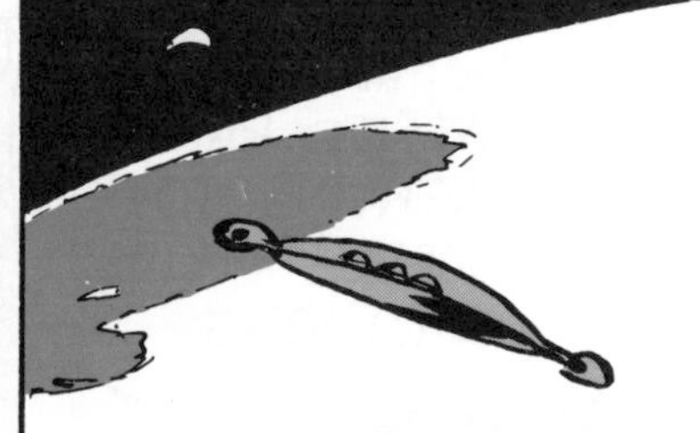

I'M NOT GOING TO SCHOOL ANY MORE.
OH?

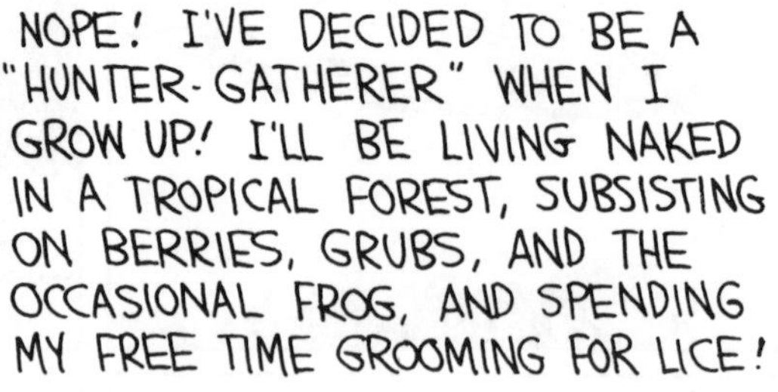
NOPE! I'VE DECIDED TO BE A "HUNTER-GATHERER" WHEN I GROW UP! I'LL BE LIVING NAKED IN A TROPICAL FOREST, SUBSISTING ON BERRIES, GRUBS, AND THE OCCASIONAL FROG, AND SPENDING MY FREE TIME GROOMING FOR LICE!

ALL THE EXPERTS SAY IT'S BAD PARENTING TO SQUELCH A KID'S AMBITIONS.

MISS WORMWOOD, I HAVE A QUESTION ABOUT THIS MATH LESSON.
YES?

GIVEN THAT, SOONER OR LATER, WE'RE ALL JUST GOING TO DIE, WHAT'S THE POINT OF LEARNING ABOUT INTEGERS?

TURN TO PAGE 83, CLASS.

NOBODY LIKES US "BIG PICTURE" PEOPLE.

THE PROBLEM WITH PEOPLE IS THEY DON'T LOOK AT THE BIG PICTURE.

EVENTUALLY, WE'RE EACH GOING TO DIE, OUR SPECIES WILL GO EXTINCT, THE SUN WILL EXPLODE, AND THE UNIVERSE WILL COLLAPSE.

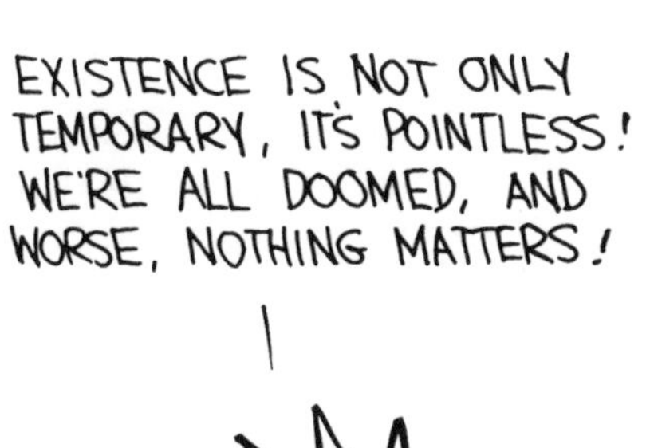
EXISTENCE IS NOT ONLY TEMPORARY, IT'S POINTLESS! WE'RE ALL DOOMED, AND WORSE, NOTHING MATTERS!

I SEE WHY PEOPLE DON'T LIKE TO LOOK AT THE BIG PICTURE.
WELL, IT PUTS A BAD DAY IN PERSPECTIVE.
WATTERSON

MISS WORMWOOD, COULD WE ARRANGE OUR SEATS IN A CIRCLE AND HAVE A LITTLE DISCUSSION?

SPECIFICALLY, I'D LIKE TO DEBATE WHETHER CANNIBALISM OUGHT TO BE GROUNDS FOR LENIENCY IN MURDERS, SINCE IT'S LESS WASTEFUL.

FOR SOME REASON, THEY'D RATHER TEACH US STUFF THAT ANY FOOL CAN LOOK UP IN A BOOK.
WATTERSON

I FLUNKED A TEST TODAY, BUT I DON'T MIND.

NO?
IT'S A QUESTION OF PRIORITIES, HOBBES. A MAN'S GOT TO MAKE ROOM FOR WHAT HE CARES ABOUT.

THESE DAYS ARE PRECIOUS, AND I'D RATHER SPEND THEM GOOFING AROUND THAN STUDYING.

I NEVER REALLY THOUGHT OF IGNORANCE AS A QUALITY OF LIFE ISSUE.
APPARENTLY, NEITHER HAS DAD.

YOU KNOW WHY BIRDS DON'T WRITE THEIR MEMOIRS? BECAUSE BIRDS DON'T LEAD EPIC LIVES, THAT'S WHY!
WHO'D WANT TO READ WHAT A BIRD DOES? NOBODY, THAT'S WHO!

THIS IS CHANGING THE SUBJECT, BUT HAVE YOU EVER NOTICED HOW SOMEBODY CAN SAY SOMETHING TOTALLY LOONY AND NOT BE AWARE OF IT? WHAT ARE YOU SUPPOSED TO DO, JUST LET IT SLIDE?!

SOMETIMES IF YOU WAIT, HE'LL TOP HIMSELF.
I SAY JUST PUNCH 'IM THEN AND THERE!

FIRST, YOU CONVINCE PEOPLE THERE'S SOMETHING WRONG WITH THEM. THAT'S EASY BECAUSE ADVERTISING HAS ALREADY CONDITIONED PEOPLE TO FEEL INSECURE ABOUT THEIR WEIGHT, LOOKS, SOCIAL STATUS, SEX APPEAL, AND SO ON.

INGENIOUS. WHAT PROBLEM WILL **YOU** HELP PEOPLE SOLVE?

THEIR ADDICTION TO SELF-HELP BOOKS!

YOU SHOULD PROBABLY WAIT FOR THE ADVANCE BEFORE YOU BUY ANYTHING.

THE TROUBLE IS... IF MY PROGRAM WORKS, I WON'T BE ABLE TO WRITE A SEQUEL.

SO ANYWAY, THERE'S THIS DOG AND HE SAYS SOMETHING ODD, I DON'T REMEMBER, BUT THIS OTHER GUY SAYS, UM, WELL, I FORGET, BUT IT WAS FUNNY.

HELLO?
HELLO. IS YOUR MOTHER HOME?

WHAT BUSINESS IS IT OF **YOURS**, JERK ?!
SLAM!

SOME PEOPLE SURE ARE NOSY.

I LEFT THREE MESSAGES TODAY, AND NOBODY RETURNED MY CALL.
HOW RUDE.

I THINK WE SHOULD GET AN ANSWERING MACHINE.
UGH, I DON'T.

IF YOU HAVE A MACHINE, YOU FEEL OBLIGATED TO RETURN A BUNCH OF CALLS YOU'D RATHER NOT HAVE RECEIVED IN THE FIRST PLACE.

WITHOUT A MACHINE, YOU CAN JUST LET THE PHONE RING, AND EVENTUALLY THE CALLER GIVES UP AND YOU DON'T HAVE TO TALK TO HIM.

THAT WASN'T QUITE MY POINT.
THAT'S THE PROBLEM AT WORK. THE SECRETARIES WON'T IGNORE THE PHONE, SO I'M ALWAYS TALKING TO PEOPLE.

THE MORE YOU THINK ABOUT THINGS, THE WEIRDER THEY SEEM.

TAKE THIS MILK. WHY DO WE DRINK **COW** MILK ??

WHO WAS THE GUY WHO FIRST LOOKED AT A COW AND SAID, "I THINK I'LL DRINK WHATEVER COMES OUT OF THESE THINGS WHEN I SQUEEZE 'EM!"?

ISN'T THAT WEIRD?
I THINK CONVERSATION SHOULD BE KEPT TO A MINIMUM UNTIL AFTERNOON.

I'VE BEEN DISEMPOWERED! MY CENTERING, SELF-ACTUALIZING ANIMA HAS BEEN IMPACTED BY TOXIC, CO-DEPENDENT DYSFUNCTIONALITY!

YOU'VE BEEN TEMPORARILY INCONVENIENCED. TAKE OUT THE TRASH.

ARE YOU SAYING THERE'S A DIFFERENCE ?!

CALVIN AND HOBBES
by WATTERSON
HELP HELP
ACK
OOF
MMF!
UMF
GAKK
RRRGGH
GRRRR
YIPE!
WAAAA!
SCREEECH
NNGG
AAAAAAAAAAAA
THANKS FOR THE HELMET, DAD. DO THEY SELL LONG-RANGE, OFFENSIVE WEAPONS?
LOOKS LIKE YOU'VE BEEN BUILDING SOME CHARACTER!

DAD, WHAT CAUSES WIND?
TREES SNEEZING.

REALLY??
NO, BUT THE TRUTH IS MORE COMPLICATED.

THE TREES ARE REALLY SNEEZING TODAY.

WHAT DO YOU THINK THAT CLOUD LOOKS LIKE?

A BUNCH OF SUSPENDED WATER AND ICE PARTICLES, ... WHY?

EVERYBODY HATES A LITERALIST.

MOM, CAN I HAVE THE CAR KEYS?
NO.

CAN YOU BELIEVE THE ENCYCLOPEDIA DOESN'T HAVE AN ENTRY FOR "HOTWIRE"?

WHEN I SPIT, I GET PRETTY GOOD SALIVA COHESION, BUT I'M STILL NOT GETTING MUCH DISTANCE OR ACCURACY.

I THINK THE PROBLEM LIES IN THE MIX OF PHLEGM. IF YOU DON'T GET THAT CRITICAL MUCUS MASS, YOU JUST...

...HOBBES?

NOBODY LIKES TO HEAR ABOUT A HOBBY.

YOU KNOW WHAT I LIKE TO DO WHEN SOMEONE'S TALKING TO ME? I STARE AT THE PERSON'S CHIN.

I'LL NOD AND RESPOND TO WHATEVER HE'S SAYING, BUT I KEEP LOOKING AT HIS CHIN AND CHANGING MY EXPRESSION.

I LOOK QUIZZICAL AT FIRST, THEN VAGUELY REPULSED, AND LATER, QUIETLY AMUSED. THEN I'LL SUDDENLY ARCH MY EYEBROWS AND BLINK A LOT, AND THEN I LOOK SKEPTICAL AND DISBELIEVING.

YOU GET BONUS POINTS EVERY TIME THE PERSON LOSES HIS TRAIN OF THOUGHT.
I'LL BET YOUR NATURAL CHARM HAS MADE YOU A GOOD SPRINTER.

Calvin and HOBBES
by WATTERSON
I LOVE SUMMER! THREE WHOLE MONTHS WITH NO RESPONSIBILITIES! THERE'S NOTHING WE HAVE TO DO!
THEY SAY IDLE HANDS ARE THE DEVIL'S WORKSHOP.
I RESENT THAT!
WE WORK DARN HARD AT THIS.
THIS WAY
Stand HERE: Get a Big SURPRISE

WHAT IF THERE'S NO AFTERLIFE? SUPPOSE THIS IS ALL WE GET.

OH, WHAT THE HECK. I'LL TAKE IT ANYWAY.
YEAH, BUT IF I'M NOT GOING TO BE ETERNALLY REWARDED FOR MY BEHAVIOR, I'D SURE LIKE TO KNOW **NOW**.

PHUP
PHUPP
PHUP
PHBBTTB

HEY, THAT WAS A **GOOD** ONE!
THANK YOU.

IT'S FUNNY HOW YOU NEVER SEE MOM AND DAD PRACTICE THESE.
PHUP
PHUP
THEY'RE PROBABLY GOOD AT IT ALREADY.

I WATCHED AN OLD MOVIE WITH MOM LAST NIGHT.

IT DIDN'T HAVE ANY VIOLENCE, EXPLOSIVE ACTION, OR SWEARING. THERE WAS NOTHING SHOCKING ABOUT IT AT ALL.

DID YOU LIKE IT?
IT'S HARD TO SAY.

NOT HAVING MY EMOTIONS MANIPULATED IS SUCH A WEIRD EXPERIENCE.

THURSday, DaY 4
LiGHt WiNds, Good HuMidity. PROGRESS SLOW. GEttiNG DiSCOURaGED.

I'M ONLY BURPiNG — Not tRULY BELCHiNG. MELLOW RoundNESS REMaiNS ELUSiVE. HaRMONics COMiNG aLONG With dEVELOPiNG aMPLitudE.
HaNG iN tHERE!

THEY SAY YOU SHOULD KEEP A LOG WHEN YOU TAKE UP A SPORT.

ARCHITECTS SHOULD BE FORCED TO LIVE IN THE BUILDINGS THEY DESIGN, AND CHILDREN'S BOOK AUTHORS SHOULD BE FORCED TO READ THEIR STORIES ALOUD EVERY SINGLE NIGHT OF THEIR ROTTEN LIVES.

calvin and HOBBES by WATTERSON
THE FEARLESS SPACEMAN SPIFF DESCENDS TOWARD THE MYSTERIOUS PLANET BELOW!
OUR HERO'S BIZARROTRON INDICATES THE PRESENCE OF ALIENS! SPIFF SETS OUT TO INVESTIGATE!

CROUCHING BEHIND A BOULDER, OUR HERO HEARS ALIEN VOICES... TALKING ABOUT *HIM*!
BLORG GABLORG SPIFF! HA HA!
SPIFF BURSTS INTO THE OPEN, DEATH RAY BLASTER BLASTING! *"I'LL GIVE YOU SOMETHING TO TALK ABOUT!"* HE YELLS!

EXCUSE ME A MOMENT.

BACK IN THE DARKNESS OF OUTER SPACE, SPIFF REFLECTS ON HIS ONE MISCALCULATION. OUR HERO RESOLVES TO REVISIT THE PLANET, *THIS* TIME WITH MORE AMMO!
NO SLEEP TONIGHT, I SEE.

MOM AND DAD SAY I SHOULD MAKE MY LIFE AN EXAMPLE OF THE PRINCIPLES I BELIEVE IN.

BUT EVERY TIME I DO, THEY TELL ME TO STOP IT.
I'M NOT SURE THAT TOTAL SELF-INDULGENCE IS REALLY A PRINCIPLE.

LIKE DELICATE LACE, SO THE THREADS INTERTWINE, OH, GOSSAMER WEB OF WOND'ROUS DESIGN! SUCH BEAUTY AND GRACE WILD NATURE PRODUCES...

UGHH, LOOK AT THE SPIDER SUCK OUT THAT BUG'S JUICES!

I READ THAT SCIENTISTS ARE TRYING TO MAKE COMPUTERS THAT **THINK**.

ISN'T THAT WEIRD?? IF COMPUTERS CAN THINK, WHAT WILL PEOPLE BE BETTER AT THAN MACHINES?

IRRATIONAL BEHAVIOR.
MAYBE THEY'LL INVENT A PSYCHOTIC COMPUTER.

I NEED A PUSH! SOMEBODY COME AND GIVE ME A PUSH!

RRRGGHHH

WHERE THE HECK IS THE MANUAL OVERRIDE?!

IF YOU STICK YOUR TONGUE OUT FOR A LONG TIME, IT DRIES UP! TRY IT!

WHY WOULD ANYONE WANT HIS TONGUE TO DRY UP?!

BECAUSE THEN IT FEELS REALLY WEIRD WHEN YOU TOUCH IT.
I'LL TAKE YOUR WORD FOR IT.

SOME PEOPLE JUST AREN'T OPEN TO REVELATORY EXPERIENCES.

ZZIZZZZ

WHIPP
FLIP
ZZZZ
ZZZZ

FWAP!
ZIPPPP
ZZZZZ

THE ONLY SKILLS I HAVE THE PATIENCE TO LEARN ARE THOSE THAT HAVE NO REAL APPLICATION IN LIFE.

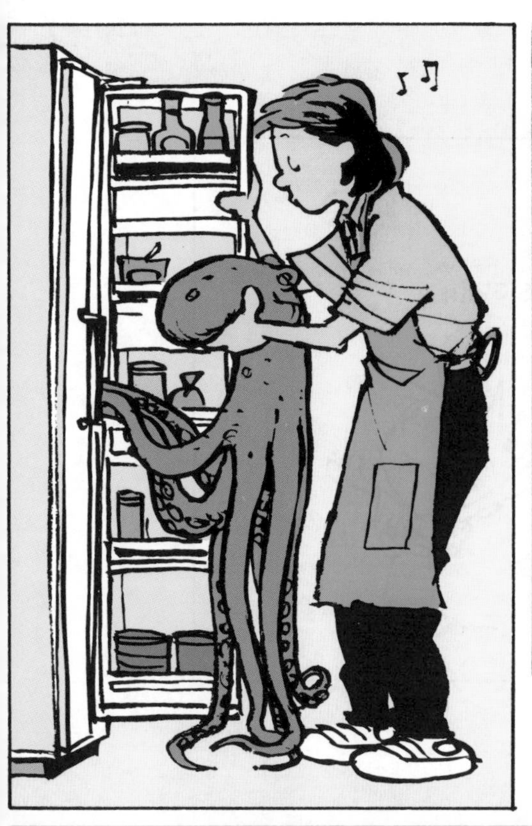

Calvin and Hobbes by WATTERSON

CAN YOU MAKE A LIVING PLAYING SILLY GAMES?
ACTUALLY, YOU CAN BE AMONG THE MOST OVERPAID PEOPLE ON THE PLANET.

..SIGHHH...

I AM THE WORLD'S MOST POWERFUL COMPUTER. ASK ME A QUESTION.

WHY DOES THE WORLD'S MOST POWERFUL COMPUTER WEAR LITTLE RED SNEAKERS?

I AM THE WORLD'S MOST POWERFUL COMPUTER. ASK ME A QUESTION.

DID CALVIN CLEAN HIS ROOM AS I ASKED HIM TO, OR DID HE SPEND THE WHOLE MORNING PLAYING WITH A CARDBOARD BOX?

UM... SYSTEM ERROR... DELETE QUESTION AND TRY AGAIN.

WHAT HAPPENED?
MOM BOOTED ME UP HERE.

FROM NOW ON, I'M NOT DOING ANYTHING I DON'T WANT TO DO!

THE WORLD OWES ME HAPPINESS, FULFILLMENT AND SUCCESS.

WELL, LUCKY YOU!
YEAH, I'M JUST HERE TO CASH IN.

WHAT ASSURANCE DO I HAVE THAT YOUR PARENTING ISN'T SCREWING ME UP?

WHERE ARE **YOU** GOING?
OUT.

DID YOU PICK UP YOUR ROOM?
I TRIED, BUT I COULDN'T LIFT IT! **GET** IT??
AH HA HA HA HA HA!

FOR SOME REASON, THE SOUND OF CHILDREN'S LAUGHTER DOESN'T MAKE MOM SENTIMENTAL.

Calvin and Hobbes
by WATTERSON

THANK YOU.
THANK *YOU*.
YEP, THERE'S NOTHING LIKE A BIG BED FOR DANCING.
I HOPE YOUR PARENTS DON'T MIND BAD SPRINGS.

GORGEOUS MORNING, HUH DAD?
MM.

THESE SUMMER DAYS SURE SLIP BY, DON'T THEY? TOO BAD THE DAILY DRUDGERY OF MAKING A LIVING HAS TO KEEP YOU FROM APPRECIATING THESE SUBLIME MOMENTS OF LIFE.

WELL, BEST NOT TO THINK ABOUT IT! IF YOU STAY HEALTHY, YOU CAN ENJOY DAYS LIKE THIS WHEN YOU RETIRE! SEE YOU TONIGHT!

AHHH, SUMMER!

LOOK WHAT I'VE GOT!
WHAT IS IT?

IT'S THE BOX A BAR OF SOAP COMES IN.

IT'S A TRADITION THAT WHEN YOU HARANGUE THE MULTITUDES, YOU STAND ON A SOAP BOX.

YOU'D PROBABLY BE MORE IMPRESSIVE IF YOU TRIED USING THE SOAP.
LET ME KNOW IF YOU SEE ANY MULTITUDES.

I HAVE A VERY SARCASTIC MOTHER.

MY ELBOWS ARE GRASS-STAINED, I'VE GOT STICKS IN MY HAIR, I'M COVERED WITH BUG BITES AND CUTS AND SCRATCHES...

I'VE GOT SAND IN MY SOCKS AND LEAVES IN MY SHIRT, MY HANDS ARE STICKY WITH SAP, AND MY SHOES ARE SOAKED! I'M HOT, DIRTY, SWEATY, ITCHY AND TIRED.

I SAY CONSIDER THIS DAY SEIZED!
TOMORROW WE'LL SEIZE THE DAY AND THROTTLE IT!

I SAW YOUR TEACHER, MISS WORMWOOD, IN THE SUPERMARKET TODAY. SHE SAID TO SAY HI.

YOU SAW MISS WORMWOOD ?? SHE SHOPS AT THE SUPERMARKET ??
WELL CERTAINLY. WHAT DID YOU THINK?

I DUNNO... I KINDA FIGURED TEACHERS SLEPT IN COFFINS ALL SUMMER.

WHAP

DON'T ASK DUMB QUESTIONS. JUST RING MY DOORBELL, HOLD THE BAT, AND YELL, "HA HA!"
WHY IS THAT WORTH TEN CENTS TO YOU?

I DON'T THINK SO.

DEFINITELY NOT.

MM.... NAHH...

THAT'S A LITTLE BETTER.

EWW.

YEAH! PERFECT!

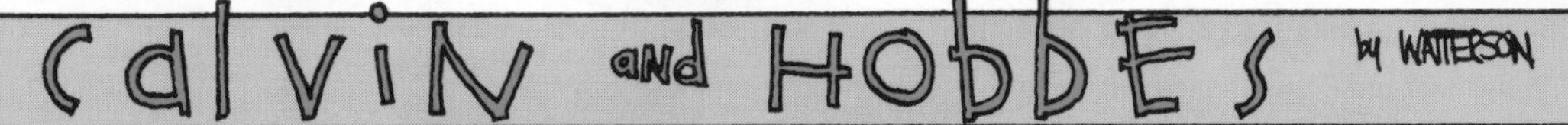
Calvin and HOBBES
by WATTERSON

WHAT NOW, CALVIN?
ASPIRIN

NO. ABSOLUTELY NOT. PUT THOSE BACK.

MOM SAYS NO WAY.
GROWN-UPS HAVE NO TASTE.
SUN GLASSES

A PAINTING OF A COMIC STRIP PANEL. SOPHISTICATED IRONY. PHILOSOPHICALLY CHALLENGING. ...."HIGH" ART.

MOMM! HEY, MOM!

CALVIN, STOP YELLING ACROSS THE HOUSE! IF YOU WANT TO TALK TO ME, WALK OVER TO THE LIVING ROOM, WHERE I AM!

I STEPPED IN DOG DOO. WHERE'S THE HOSE?

HERE'S A BUG PLODDING RESOLUTELY ACROSS THE DIRT.

PUT A ROCK IN HIS WAY, AND HE JUST GOES AROUND IT. FLIP HIM ON HIS BACK, AND HE RIGHTS HIMSELF AND CONTINUES ON HIS WAY. HE'S FOCUSED, DETERMINED, AND STEADFAST.

IF HE'S MOCKING ME, I'M GONNA GOOSH HIM.

YOWP! AHH!
OOH!

WHAT A DUMB RIDE. ON THE HOTTEST DAYS YOU NEED THE HEAVIEST PANTS.

I HATE GOING TO BED BEFORE IT'S DARK OUT! IT'S NOT FAIR!

I'LL SHOW MOM AND DAD, THOUGH! THEY'LL PAY FOR THIS!

IF I HAVE TO GO TO BED WHILE IT'S STILL LIGHT, THEN I'M GOING TO GET UP WHEN IT'S STILL DARK!

A SOLITARY ZOKK CIRCLES HIGH IN THE SWELTERING SKIES OF A DESERT PLANET. BELOW, A THIN PLUME OF SMOKE RISES FROM THE WRECKAGE OF A SMALL, RED SPACECRAFT!

Calvin and Hobbes
by WATTERSON
OUR HERO, THE INTREPID SPACEMAN SPIFF, CRAWLS ACROSS THE SUN-BAKED LAND! HE..HE MUST FIND SH-SHELTER!
WAIT! SOMETHING IS APPROACHING! IS IT A MIRAGE??

GOODNESS, PUT ON SOME SUN SCREEN AND WEAR A HAT IF YOU'RE GOING TO BE OUT HERE.

HONESTLY. SHOW A LITTLE COMMON SENSE.

AND DON'T GIVE ME THAT LOOK.

SPIFF SURVIVES, FIXES HIS SHIP AND SETS OFF TO FIND A MORE TEMPERATE PLANET WITH FEWER ALIENS.

JUMP JUMP JUMP JUMP JUMP JUMP JUMP JUMP!

AHH, YOU'VE FALLEN INTO MY TRAP! MAYBE YOU'D LIKE TO TAKE THAT MOVE OVER!
YOUR REMAINING PIECE MUST HAVE ONE HECK OF A PLAN.

THESE REAL-LIFE VIDEO PROGRAMS ARE GREAT!

HERE ARE ORDINARY PEOPLE HAVING ACTUAL, HORRIBLE EXPERIENCES, WHICH ARE BROADCAST NATIONWIDE FOR THE PUBLIC'S VIEWING AMUSEMENT!

IT'S INTRUSION, EXPLOITATION, AND VOYEURISM ALL IN ONE! YOU NEVER KNOW WHERE A VIDEO CAMERA WILL BE!
EVERYTHING'S FAIR GAME!

WHO'D HAVE GUESSED BIG BROTHER WOULD GO COMMERCIAL?
I LOVE TO SNICKER AT OTHER PEOPLE'S TRAGEDY.

DAD, WHAT'S A CONTROL FREAK?

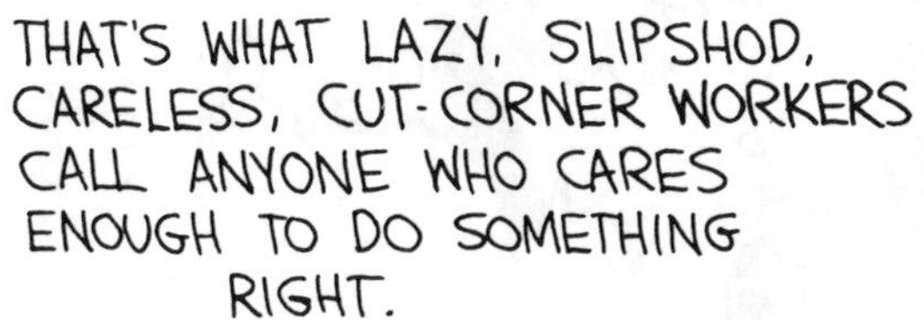
THAT'S WHAT LAZY, SLIPSHOD, CARELESS, CUT-CORNER WORKERS CALL ANYONE WHO CARES ENOUGH TO DO SOMETHING RIGHT.

AM I IN THE PRESENCE OF THEIR KING? SHOULD I KNEEL?
IF ANYTHING WORKS IN THIS WORLD, IT'S BECAUSE ONE OF US TOOK CHARGE.

SPLOOSH!

AAA! NO! WAIT! THINK ABOUT IT! WASN'T THAT **REFRESHING**??

I NEED TO WORK ON MY SALESMANSHIP.

MOM SAYS IF I STAY UP HERE FOR TWO HOURS, THREE DAYS A WEEK, I DON'T HAVE TO TAKE ANY LESSONS THIS SUMMER.

I LIKE PEOPLE. I'M INTERESTED IN PEOPLE.

YOU??

AS AN AUDIENCE, I MEAN.
OH.

Calvin and Hobbes

by WATTERSON

Calvin and Hobbes
by WATTERSON
A BEE NEST! I HATE BEES!
WHAP
ZZZZZZZ
AIEE!
AAAAAAAAAA
YOWW!
I DON'T SEE THE "HARPOON" THAT "GORED" YOU, BUT THIS WILL HELP THE STING.
CALL THE NATIONAL GUARD. I'M SURE THEY CAN TRACK THE BEE ON RADAR.

THIS MEETING OF THE GET RID OF SLIMY GIRLS CLUB WILL NOW COME TO ORDER! FIRST TIGER HOBBES WILL READ THE MINUTES OF OUR LAST MEETING.

THANK YOU. "9:30 - MEETING CALLED TO ORDER. DICTATOR-FOR-LIFE CALVIN PROPOSES RESOLUTION CONDEMNING EXISTENCE OF GIRLS."

"9:35 - FIRST TIGER ABSTAINS FROM VOTE. MOTION FAILS. 9:36 - PATRIOTISM OF FIRST TIGER CALLED INTO QUESTION. 9:37 - PHILOSOPHICAL DISCUSSION. 10:15 - BANDAGES ADMINISTERED. DICTATOR-FOR-LIFE REBUKED FOR BITING."

IS THIS A GREAT CLUB, OR WHAT?
"10:16 - FORGOT WHAT DEBATE WAS ABOUT. MEDALS OF BRAVERY AWARDED TO ALL PARTIES."

GENTLEMEN, THE PURPOSE OF TODAY'S MEETING IS TO DEVISE ANOTHER BRILLIANT PLAN TO ANNOY OUR ENEMY!
"DICTATOR-FOR-LIFE CALVIN'S BOLD PROPOSAL IS GREETED WITH HUZZAHS FROM MEMBERSHIP."

WE HAVE TOLERATED THE ENEMY'S PRESENCE TOO LONG, I SAY!
"SHOUTS OF ASSENT. MUCH POUNDING ON TABLES. THREE CHEERS ERUPT FOR CLUB IDEALS. MEMBERSHIP REDUCED TO TEARS. MORE HUZZAHS. PANDEMONIUM ENSUES."

BOY, LEADING A CLUB IS A HEADY EXPERIENCE.
GOOD MEETINGS ALWAYS TURN INTO RIOTS.

FIELD SCOUT CALVIN REPORTS THE ENEMY WAS SIGHTED, ENGAGED IN ENEMY ACTIVITY, ON THE SIDEWALK TWO DOORS DOWN.

AS CHIEF STRATEGIST, I SUGGEST...
EXCUSE ME. A QUESTION FROM THE FLOOR.

THE CHAIR RECOGNIZES FIRST TIGER HOBBES.
EXACTLY WHAT "ENEMY ACTIVITY" WAS THE ENEMY ENGAGED IN?

YOU KNOW, GIRL STUFF!
AH. SAY NO MORE.

ALL RIGHT, HERE'S THE PLAN! WE MAKE UP A FAKE CODE WITH FAKE INSTRUCTIONS AND SEE THAT IT "ACCIDENTALLY" FALLS INTO SUSIE'S HANDS!

SHE DECODES THE MESSAGE, WHICH SAYS WE **DON'T** WANT HER TO GO BEHIND OUR HOUSE! NATURALLY, SHE'LL GO THERE, AND WE'LL BE WAITING, READY TO SOAK HER WITH WATER BALLOONS!

WHY DON'T WE JUST HIT HER WITH WATER BALLOONS RIGHT NOW, WHERE SHE'S SITTING?

YOU'RE A GOOD OFFICER, HOBBES, BUT LET'S FACE IT, YOU DON'T HAVE AN EXECUTIVE MIND.
I STILL THINK MY IDEA **SORT** OF MAKES SENSE...

NOW THIS IS SUPPOSED TO LOOK LIKE A CODED MESSAGE FROM ME TO YOU, BUT WE'LL LEAVE IT FOR SUSIE TO FIND.

OBVIOUSLY, THE CODE WILL HAVE TO BE EASY TO BREAK, SO SHE CAN READ THE DISINFORMATION WE'RE GIVING HER.

HOW ABOUT IF WE WRITE BACKWARDS?
YEAH, THAT'S GOOD!

DEAR HOBBES,
GOSH, I HOPE SUSIE'S NOT TOO DUMB TO FIGURE THIS OUT.
CRACKING CODES IS SECOND NATURE TO COOL SPIES LIKE US.
WATTERSON

TOP SECRET!!
DEAR HOBBES,
IF SUSIE GOES BEHIND OUR HOUSE AT NOON, ALL OUR SECRET PLANS WILL BE RUINED!
CALVIN

THERE! ONCE SUSIE DECODES THIS MESSAGE, SHE'LL BE LURED TO OUR WATER BALLOON TRAP! WHAT A GREAT PLAN!

MY ONLY REGRET IS BLOWING THE BEST DAY OF MY LIFE WHILE I'M SO YOUNG.
WATTERSON

GOOD! SUSIE'S STILL PLAYING ON THE SIDEWALK! WE'LL STROLL BY AND "ACCIDENTALLY" DROP THE CODED MESSAGE.

YES HOBBES, I HAVE A **TOP SECRET, CODED** LETTER FOR YOU HERE! VERRRRY MYSTERIOUS! VERRRRY SECRET!

JUST MAKE SURE THE NOTE DOESN'T FALL INTO A **GIRL'S** HANDS! IF THE CODE IS BROKEN AND READ, OUR PLANS WILL BE RUINED!

WE DID IT! HA! EVERYTHING IS GOING PERFECTLY!
..EXCEPT SHE'S NOT PICKING UP THE LETTER.

WHY ISN'T SUSIE PICKING UP THE CODED MESSAGE?! DOESN'T SHE **SEE** IT??

WHAT'S **WRONG** WITH HER?! DOESN'T SHE KNOW ENOUGH TO INTERCEPT SOMEBODY ELSE'S SECRET LETTER WHEN IT'S DROPPED RIGHT IN FRONT OF HER??

MAYBE SHE WASN'T PAYING ATTENTION TO US.
THAT'S INCONCEIVABLE! WHO WOULDN'T BE INTERESTED IN EVERYTHING WE DO?!

LOOK! SUSIE SEES THE LETTER! SHE'S PICKING IT UP! SHE'S READING THE ENVELOPE!

... SHE'S WALKING OVER HERE ...

YOU DROPPED THIS LETTER FOR HOBBES. HERE.
UM... GEE, THANKS.

WELL, THAT WAS AWFULLY DECENT OF HER.
IT'S NO USE! IT'S NO USE! EVERYBODY GETS GOOD ENEMIES, EXCEPT **ME**!

LET'S STROLL OVER **THIS** WAY **ONCE AGAIN**, HOBBES!
YES, LET'S!

IT'S A GOOD THING YOU HAVE THAT **TOP SECRET, CODED** LETTER, HOBBES! IT WOULD BE AWFUL IF YOU HAPPENED TO **DROP** IT NEAR **SUSIE** ONE MORE TIME!

IF I WERE **SUSIE**, AND I **FOUND THE LETTER**, I'D **PICK IT UP AND DECODE IT**, SO I COULD **RUIN ALL OUR PLANS!** THAT WOULD SURE BE **BAD** FOR **US**!

IT WORKED! SHE'S OPENING THE LETTER!
GOOD. I WAS AFRAID WE'D HAVE TO HIT HER ON THE HEAD AND READ IT TO HER.

THIS MUST BE THE CODED LETTER CALVIN'S TRYING TO GET ME TO READ. HMPH, NOT MUCH OF A CODE... JUST BACKWARD LETTERS! I CAN READ IT THROUGH THE BACK OF THE PAGE.

IT'S PAST NOON! WHY ISN'T SUSIE WALKING INTO OUR BRILLIANT AMBUSH?! WHERE IS SHE?!

YOU STAY HERE AND GUARD THE WATER BALLOONS. I'LL GO ON A RECONNAISSANCE MISSION AND FIND OUT WHAT SHE'S DOING.

WAIT A MINUTE. WHY CAN'T *I* GO ON THE RECONNAISSANCE MISSION?

BECAUSE IF YOU GOT CAPTURED, YOU'D TELL SUSIE ANYTHING FOR A TUMMY RUB.
I **MIGHT** NOT!

YOU CAN'T TRUST A GIRL TO DO ***ANYTHING*** RIGHT! WE GO TO ALL THIS TROUBLE TO LURE SUSIE INTO A TRAP, AND SHE DOESN'T SHOW UP!

AS SOON AS I FIND OUT WHERE SHE IS, I'LL GET HOBBES AND THE WATER BALLOONS AND WE'LL LET HER HAVE IT!

IF SHE WON'T COME TO THE AMBUSH, WE'LL BRING THE AMBUSH TO HER!
FIVE... FOUR... THREE... TWO...

AAUGH! OH NO! AIEE! ACKPTH! PBLBTH! BLUBPLUB PLPPTTB!

THIS DOESN'T GO IN THE CLUB LOG, UNDERSTOOD? IT NEVER HAPPENED.
SINCE YOU'RE ALREADY WET, IT WOULD BE A SHAME NOT TO USE THESE WATER BALLOONS.

IT'S A DARK DAY FOR THE GET RID OF SLIMY GIRLS CLUB.

OUR GREAT PLAN BACKFIRED AND I'M THE ONE WHO GOT SOAKED! OH, THE SHAME! THE IGNOMINY!

..SIGHHHH...

IF YOU RESIGN, CAN I BE DICTATOR-FOR-LIFE?
I DIDN'T SAY I WAS RESIGNING!

WELL HOBBES, THE BATTLE MAY HAVE BEEN LOST, BUT THE WAR GOES ON!

THIS AFTERNOON, WE'LL DEVISE A BIGGER, BETTER, AND EVEN MORE COMPLICATED SCHEME, AND REVENGE WILL BE OURS! THE SPIRIT OF G.R.O.S.S.NESS CANNOT BE EXTINGUISHED!

...AND FOR COURAGE IN THE FACE OF TEMPORARY SETBACKS, I AWARD US BOTTLE CAPS OF VALOR!
YAYY!

A GOOD MEETING ALWAYS ENDS WITH US GETTING NEW MEDALS!
THIS IS SUCH A GREAT CLUB!

HERE CALVIN, I BROUGHT SOME LUNCH FOR YOU AND HOBBES.
GEE THANKS, MOM.

WHAT DO YOU SAY WE BREAK OUT THE COMIC BOOKS WHILE WE THINK UP OUR BIG PLANS?
OH BOY!

IT'S LOOKING LIKE A GOOD AFTERNOON, OL' BUDDY.
I LOVE SUMMER.

Calvin and Hobbes by Watterson

THIS IS DAD'S IDEA OF TAKING US TO THE BEACH.

YEP, THAT'S A PRETTY GOOD COW IMPRESSION.
FROM NOW ON, THAT'S HOW I EAT SALADS.

Calvin and HOBBES by WATTERSON
I WISH WE COULD STOP SUMMER RIGHT HERE AND HAVE THE DAYS STAY JUST THE WAY THEY ARE.

THAT'S THE PROBLEM WITH LIFE. IT ROLLS ALONG WITH SPEED YOU CAN'T CONTROL. YOU CAN'T GO FASTER OR SLOWER.

FUN EXPERIENCES ALWAYS GO ROARING BY.

...WHILE BAD EXPERIENCES NEVER PASS QUICKLY ENOUGH.

I WISH WE COULD CHOOSE HOW FAST AND SLOW EVENTS GO.

FOR EXAMPLE, I'D LIKE TO SPEED UP CHILDHOOD AND GET TO DRIVING AGE.
IT'S NOT THE PACE OF LIFE I MIND. IT'S THE SUDDEN STOP AT THE END.

ALL RIGHT, HERE'S A NICKEL. WHAT DO I GET?
LIFE 5¢

NOTHING. I JUST RIPPED YOU OFF.
WHAT?!
LIFE

THAT'S LIFE!
LIFE

HEY! OW! OW!

OH, MOM? I JUST REMEMBERED. SOME LADY CALLED YOU ABOUT AN HOUR AGO.
DID YOU GET HER NAME AND NUMBER?

NO...
WELL HOW AM I SUPPOSED TO CALL HER BACK?!

YOU DON'T NEED TO. SHE'S STILL ON THE LINE.

NOTHING FOR ME...
NOTHING FOR ME...

PHOOEY.

THE MAIL'S HERE.

YESTERDAY DAD TOLD ME NOT TO EAT A PEPPER BECAUSE IT WAS HOT, ... SO I ATE THE WHOLE THING IN TWO BITES.

MAN, WAS I EVER IN AGONY! I WAS RICOCHETING OFF THE WALLS ALL NIGHT! I THOUGHT I WAS GOING TO EXPLODE!

I GOTTA GET A STUNT DOUBLE.

calvin and HOBBES

by WATTERSON

SUMMER DAYS ARE SUPPOSED TO BE LONGER, BUT THEY SURE SEEM SHORT TO **ME**.

I'LL SAY. WE DIDN'T GET TO DO HALF OUR ITINERARY.